D0577808

KARAKUM SANDS UNDER A STORMY SKY

CONIFER VALLEY IN KIRGIZIA

PARCHED HILLS IN THE KARAKUM

SAND BANKS IN A PAMIR LAKE

SALT PANS (BACKGROUND) AT THE SOUTHERN EDGE OF THE KARAKUM

SNOW PATCHES ON A HIGH PAMIR PASS

CHISELLED OUTCROPPINGS IN THE TIEN SHAN FOOTHILLS

STORM OVER WIND-WHIPPED LAKE ISSYK-KUL

LIBRARY OF NATIONS
CLASSICS OF EXPLORATION
PLANET EARTH
PEOPLES OF THE WILD
THE EPIC OF FLIGHT
THE SEAFARERS
WORLD WAR II
THE GOOD COOK
THE TIME-LIFE ENCYCLOPAEDIA
OF GARDENING
THE GREAT CITIES
THE OLD WEST
THE WORLD'S WILD PLACES
THE EMERGENCE OF MAN
LIFE LIBRARY OF PHOTOGRAPHY
TIME-LIFE LIBRARY OF ART
GREAT AGES OF MAN
LIFE SCIENCE LIBRARY
LIFE NATURE LIBRARY
THE TIME-LIFE BOOK OF BOATING
TECHNIQUES OF PHOTOGRAPHY
LIFE AT WAR
LIFE GOES TO THE MOVIES
BEST OF LIFE
LIFE IN SPACE

# SOVIET DESERTS AND MOUNTAINS

**THE WORLD'S WILD PLACES/TIME-LIFE BOOKS/AMSTERDAM**

BY GEORGE ST. GEORGE
AND THE EDITORS OF TIME-LIFE BOOKS

WITH PHOTOGRAPHS BY LEV USTINOV,
NOVOSTI PRESS AGENCY, MOSCOW

© 1974 Time-Life Books B.V.
All rights reserved. Sixth English printing 1984.

Editorial Staff for *Soviet Deserts and Mountains*:
EDITOR: John Man
*Deputy Editor*: Simon Rigge
*Picture Editor*: Pamela Marke
*Design Consultant*: Louis Klein
*Staff Writers*:
Michael Brown, Mally Cox, Kate Dorment,
Tony Long, Timberlake Wertenbaker,
Heather Wyatt
*Picture Researchers*: Kerry Arnold,
Karin Pearce
*Art Director*: Graham Davis
*Design Assistant*: Joyce Mason
*Editorial Co-ordinator*: Vanessa Kramer
*Editorial Assistant*: Jackie Matthews

Consultants
*Botany*: Phyllis Edwards
*Desert Ecology*: Prof. J. Cloudsley-Thompson
*Geology*: Dr. Peter Stubbs, Dr. Andrew Warren
*Herpetology*: David Ball
*Zoology*: Dr. P. J. K. Burton
*Book Consultant*: Dr. Leslie Symons

Valuable assistance was given in the preparation of
this volume by John Shaw and Felix Rosenthal of the
Time-Life News Service, Moscow.

No part of this book may be reproduced in any form
or by any electronic or mechanical means, including
information storage and retrieval devices or systems,
without prior written permission from the publisher,
except that brief passages may be quoted for review.

ISBN 7054 0097 2

TIME-LIFE is a trademark
of Time Incorporated U.S.A.

Published by Time-Life Books B.V.
Ottho Heldringstraat 5, 1066 AZ Amsterdam.

George St. George, formerly roving editor of the conservationist magazine *International Wildlife*, grew up in Siberia and spent much of his youth travelling throughout Asia and the Far East. After working as actor and film-writer in the United States, he moved to Paris. Besides several articles and television and stage plays, he has written a number of novels and non-fictional books dealing with his native Russia including *Siberia, the New Frontier, Russian Folk Medicine, The Road to Babyi Yar* and *Our Soviet Sister.*

Leslie Symons, the consultant on this book, is Professor of Geography at the University College of Swansea, where he contributes to the teaching and research of the Centre of Russian and East European Studies. His books include *Land Use in Northern Ireland, Agricultural Geography*, a series of booklets on the geography of the U.S.S.R., *Russian Agriculture—A Geographic Survey* and, as co-author, *Russian Transport.* He has travelled in most parts of the Soviet Union and is particularly interested in the mountainous areas of Central Asia and the Caucasus.

*The cover*: A weirdly contorted mountain plateau in the Karakum desert is whitened by remnants of former seas: layers of gypsum and salt embedded in terraced shale. Over the centuries flash floods have shaped the landscape, planing smooth the area in the centre and cutting a mass of wrinkled gullies into the plateau rim in the foreground.

# Contents

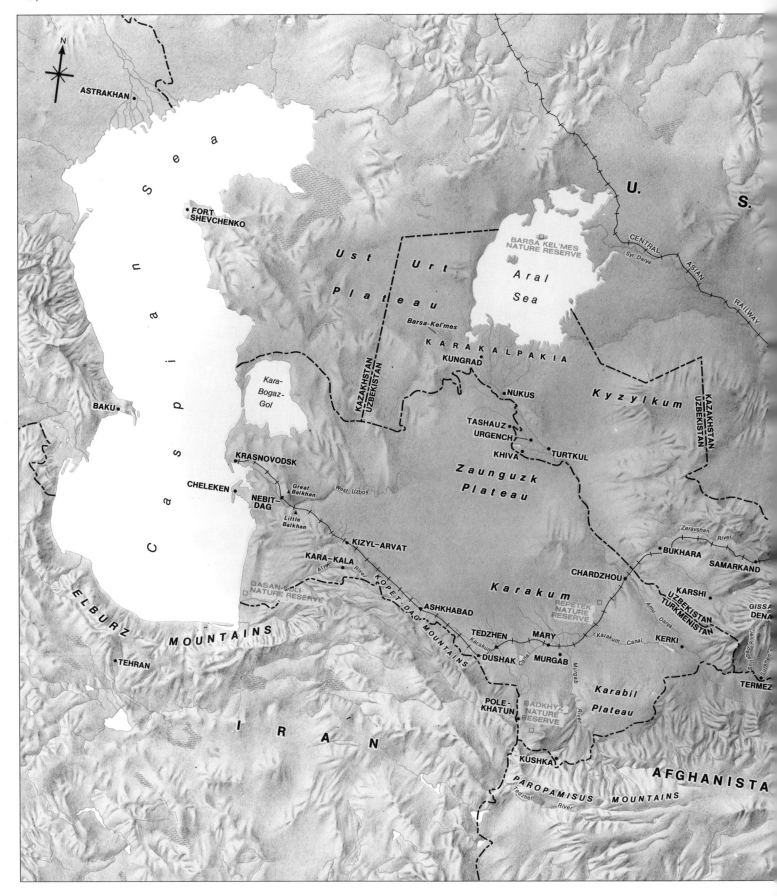

## From Desert Lowlands To Ice-Bound Peaks

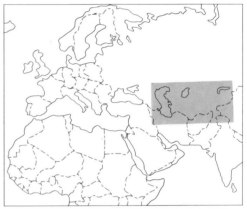

The desert, foothill and mountain wilderness shown in the shaded rectangle (above) forms a geographical bridge between the Middle East and the Far East. The 700,000 square mile area that is the subject of this book is mapped in detail (in colour, left). Stretching east of the Caspian Sea across the four Soviet Socialist Republics that border Iran, Afghanistan and China, it is a land of extremes. In the west, two deserts—the Karakum and the Kyzylkum (brown)—make up the fourth largest desert area in the world. Moving east, desert gives way to the fertile foothills (green) of the two towering mountain ranges, the Pamirs and the Tien Shan (yellow). Here massive glaciers feed two rivers, the Amu Darya and the Syr Darya, that slice across the whole area to empty into the Aral Sea. Nature Reserves are marked with red squares.

# 1/ An Arid Borderland

*Something of marvel must there be in a country which
presents to the eye a succession of bewildering contrasts;
where grandeur alternates with sadness; where the scarp of
precipitous mountains frowns over an unending plain.*

GEORGE N. CURZON/ *RUSSIA IN CENTRAL ASIA*

"But we have no wilderness," asserted my friend. He was well-connected in Moscow, and I had just suggested to him the idea of writing about Turkestan, the vast "wilderness" that lies between the Caspian Sea and the Chinese border. "We are a very advanced industrial state," he continued earnestly.

"Of course," I said, "but there are places still little touched by man. When I was in Siberia . . . "

"Now there's a fantastic place, booming with progress. Did you see the Krasnoyarsk dam?"

"I did," I said, "and I also visited Yakutia . . . "

"The land of the future!"

"Yes, but at present there is only one person for every 50 square miles of territory."

"Wait 50 years. It will be one enormous industrial complex."

"No," I said firmly, "I'm doing a book on Turkestan. After all it's one of the remotest, least known areas left on earth."

My friend's face showed his unhappiness.

"First of all," he said, "Turkestan is a name of the past. This area of Russia is today Soviet Central Asia and is composed of four Soviet Socialist Republics, Turkmenistan, Uzbekistan, Tadzhikistan and Kirgizia, and part of a fifth, Kazakhstan. Then, you really cannot call these wilderness areas. They are all advanced, agrarian-industrial states."

"But," I protested, "historically, 'Turkestan' is a perfectly justifiable term for the whole region and it is still in common use outside the Soviet Union. Besides, there are deserts there to rival the Sahara, and mountains to equal the Andes."

My friend wrinkled his brow. "Well, whatever you do, don't call it a wilderness. It is a bad word with us. It was a wilderness before the Great October Revolution, but not today."

"If it's just a matter of terminology, we could call it 'virgin nature'," I ventured.

"Hmm . . . " my friend said.

"And surely the preservation of the natural beauty and grandeur of the country is part of socialist planned management, isn't it?" I pressed on.

"Of course," said my friend, brightening. "A wilderness must be developed, but virgin nature is the people's heritage. Yes!"

"And besides," I continued, playing on the Russian love of superlatives, "this territory constitutes one of the largest and most spectacular natural wonderlands left on earth."

To drive my point home, I pulled out a map and spread it on the table.

"What a tremendous country," mused my companion. "We have certainly got everything, haven't we?"

"You have," I said, "including one of the largest deserts on earth—the Karakum—right here between the Caspian Sea and the Amu Darya river."

"Wait, wait," my friend said, poring over the map. "If we added the Kyzylkum desert, over to the east, between the Amu Darya and the Syr Darya rivers and put them both together, it would be the greatest desert on earth, wouldn't it?"

I was beginning to win my point. "No, not quite, but look up here, between the Caspian and Aral Seas. The Ust Urt Plateau. If we throw it into the pot, we might be able to come near the Sahara!" (I later found out that I was being over-optimistic: the area is one-fifth the size of the Sahara and is the world's fourth largest desert.)

By this time my friend was fully won over. "Do you want me to telephone them down there and tell them to take care of you and to show you around?"

I knew what this would mean: Vodka-studded lunches, tours of machine-building plants, *Swan Lake* performed by the Ashkhabad Ballet, and *Eugene Onegin* sung in Uzbek. Politely, I declined.

"As you wish," my friend said. "But please don't call it a wilderness.

And try to mention that we were the first people in space."

I promised that I would try, and left to plan the final details of my trip.

"Virgin nature" may sound rather heavy handed, but the term is justified when applied to Turkestan. The area's 700,000 square miles are among the most virgin on earth. This crescent of land, which nestles in Russia's vast underbelly and sweeps around from the Caspian Sea to border Iran, Afghanistan and China, encloses a desolate region, fully four-fifths of which is uninhabitable. Away from the rivers and lush foothills that have nourished successive civilizations, the traveller must contend with wind-swept dunes, canyons, plateaux of lunar-like rocks, hills pitted by hot springs, and towering mountain walls that rise to over 20,000 feet, supporting some of the mightiest glaciers on earth.

In the west Turkestan is bordered by the salt-encrusted shores of the Caspian, in the east by the forbidding peaks of the Tien Shan. In between lies a desert area that is 800 miles wide and 600 miles across from north to south. Although the great Amu Darya and Syr Darya rivers slice across the rock and sand to empty into the Aral Sea in the north, this wilderness is so barren and hostile that the rivers seem only thin veins in a vast marble slab. The high mountain ranges, which border Turkestan to the south and east, prevent precious water and cooling winds from reaching the desert, creating a climate of extremes. In the summer months the temperatures on the Karakum and Kyzylkum deserts occasionally reach 130° F., while in January cold Siberian winds spilling down across Turkestan from the Kazakh steppes often send the thermometers plunging to —15° F.

To get to know this wilderness—forgive me, my Russian friend, but the word is not so pejorative in English—was a challenge indeed. Especially for me. I am over 70, and I am shortish and quite stout. Why would I want to go tramping across deserts at my advanced age instead of peacefully fishing for perch in my favourite stream in France? That is the question I was asked before I left and have been asked constantly since my return. The answer is that the idea of going to Central Asia stirred something deep within me: it evoked long-buried memories of stories told to me as a child.

When I was a small boy I lived with my four brothers in the dreary Siberian town of Chita, some 250 miles beyond Lake Baikal. To me and my brothers, as to all Russian children of my generation, the name "Turkestan" spelled romance, challenge and danger. This was especially true for us, for just after the turn of the century, before I was born, my father, then a young Cossack officer, served briefly in Turkestan. He lived a tempestuous life—from Turkestan he went to Manchuria to fight the Japanese, joined a plot to do away with the Tsar, was banished to Siberia, fled to China, converted to Buddhism and finally died in a monastery near Harbin. His over-dramatized stories of adventure—especially those about Turkestan—fired our childish imaginations.

He told us of monstrous sand storms blotting out the sun, of waterless deserts in which Russian soldiers died of thirst or the lethal bites of poisonous spiders that lurked in every sand dune, of fierce native warriors who seemed to materialize out of nowhere on swift desert chargers to decimate the Christian infidels. We heard about snow-capped mountains, about streams swallowed by the desert sands, about exotic animals and plants, about fabulous cities in the desert where Muslim tyrants maintained magnificent palaces and harems. In my father's stories these fierce leaders possessed swarms of slaves, whom they bought and sold and slaughtered. A woman could, he assured us, be murdered by her husband for nothing more than allowing a stranger to gaze upon her face.

My father's old batman, Nikita, was less poetic in his reminiscences, and described the place more pungently. "It's no place for a civilized Christian man," he would grumble. "All the women wear black sacks over them from top to toe, and there's no way of knowing what's inside. People are eaten up by snakes and poisoned by spiders. When you're out in the wilds, you daren't leave camp to relieve yourself without taking a loaded rifle. But mostly it's the climate that's bad—by day you're baked by the sun, by night you can freeze to death on the very same spot."

My father died, Nikita died, my four brothers died, but the romantic childhood stories lived on, until now at last I was to have a chance to measure them against reality. My early fantasies should, I suppose, have disappeared as I learned more of Turkestan over the years. But somehow my increasing knowledge of the place—especially of its past—served only to heighten its lure.

The history of Turkestan—a territory that once included Chinese Turkestan, now incorporated into the province of Sinkiang—is the story of many generations of conquerors: Greek, Chinese, Turkish, Arab, Mongol, Persian and finally Russian. In the 4th Century B.C., Alexander the Great established a period of Greek-dominated rule which lasted for 150 years. In the 8th Century A.D., invading Arabs introduced Islam, the religion of many local inhabitants today. In 1218 Turkestan was seized by the Mongols under Ghenghis Khan, and after the collapse of his empire 150 years later, Turkestan experienced a golden age under Timur the Lame, better known in the West as Tamerlane. Though a cripple and half blind, he created his own empire, with Samarkand as his capital. It became a major centre of learning and culture as well as the richest and most splendid city in Central Asia.

When Tamerlane died in 1405, no single leader could hope to control the vast territory he left behind. Turkestan gradually disintegrated into a hive of warring tribes and rival states. Finally in 1762 the eastern area of Turkestan, under the Manchu Dynasty, broke off and became permanently a part of China, while the western part—the subject of this book—was split between three rival "Khanates", or centres of government. At the beginning of the 19th Century, Russia made plans to bring Turkestan into the imperial orbit. These plans had some strategic validity: Britain was expanding her Indian Empire and, it was feared, might present a threat to Russia's southern borders. While Britain began to seek protection for India by extending her influence through the Punjab into Afghanistan, Russia advanced southwards and between 1864 and 1885 she annexed most of the Central Asian heartland. Russian Turkestan remained the official title of this area until after the Revolution, when, as my Muscovite friend had explained, the separate republics of Turkmenistan, Uzbekistan, Tadzhikistan, Kirgizia and Kazakhstan were established.

Since then man has made little impact on the remoter regions of Turkestan. However, the huge mineral and natural gas resources of Turkestan are being rapidly developed by the Soviets, and the increasing energy requirements of Soviet industry have given tremendous impetus to geological research throughout the area. One result of these studies is that we now know, in general terms, how Turkestan's awesome landscape came to be formed.

Four major geological events, which overlap chronologically and are interrelated, explain the formation of Turkestan's modern landscape. The first of these, occurring some 500 million years ago when the world's shifting continental masses were in very different positions, was the formation of a vast sea that stretched from western Europe across to China. This sea also extended far to the south, to the northern shores of India, which was then a separate land-mass hundreds of miles south of its present latitude. Over a period of 100 million years sedimentary rock was continually carried by rivers into this sea, and it is this ancient rock that still underlies Turkestan. The theory that Turkestan was once an enormous tropical sea bed is still relatively new, but it acquired irrefu-

*This idealized 16th-Century Italian portrait of Tamerlane has given him the good looks and imposing dress that, in the artist's eyes, epitomized the nobility of an Emperor whose realm, two centuries earlier, had stretched from the Red Sea to northern India. The fact is that Tamerlane was a half-blind cripple known to his contemporaries as "the ugliest man in history".*

table support when in late 1973 Soviet geologists, probing for oil, discovered an extended network of coral reefs more than a mile below the surface of the Karakum desert.

Then, about 60 million years ago, the Indian sub-continent collided with the Asian land mass. The impact crumpled the layers of sedimentary rock along the edges of the two continents, creating a line of colossal mountain ranges, among them the Pamirs, the Tien Shan and the Himalayas. The newly-formed mountains trapped the sea to the north, creating a huge inland basin. As the welding of India to Central Asia continued over the next 25 million years, this basin was wedged up by the edge of the Indian land mass and was drained to the west—into the present-day Black Sea and the Mediterranean—leaving in Turkestan only a few large salty "puddles", among them the Caspian and Aral Seas.

The last two great events in the creation of Turkestan's landscape—the formation of its rivers and its present climate—were in part a result of the crumpling of the strata, and their elevation into high mountain ranges. The enormous masses of snow and ice collected on the mountains melted each spring and the melt-water that flowed down from the mountains amalgamated into a series of rivers. By far the largest of these became the Oxus (now called the Amu Darya) and the Jaxartes (the Syr Darya), still among the mightiest rivers in Central Asia. As the rivers meandered over the plains of Turkestan, their banks were regularly broken by spring floods. The water that spilled from the river-beds repeatedly found new routes. Each time these rivers changed their course they swept alluvial deposits over the dried out surfaces like a broom, laying down soft beds of potentially fertile material.

It was Turkestan's combination of heat and aridity that transformed these alluvial beds into sand. With dry winds prevailing from the vast bulk of land to the north and east, the soil could not sustain the plant life necessary to anchor it. The soil dried out and succumbed to the erosive action of the wind, which picked up loose debris and sandblasted the landscape into irredeemable bleakness.

The violent movements that have created Central Asia are by no means finished. Earthquakes, signs that the huge wedge of India is still slowly being driven underneath Asia, are a recurring feature of life in Turkestan: an average of over three tremors occurs daily throughout the year. The most recent disaster occurred in April 1966, when Tashkent, the largest city in Uzbekistan, was shaken by an earthquake so strong that more than 1,000 tremors were registered after the initial shock. Earlier, in 1948, an earthquake destroyed Ashkhabad, the capital of Turkmenistan. Ashkhabad lies on the very edge of the Karakum, and was traditionally known as the gateway to the desert. It was from this city, now rebuilt, that I had planned to begin my journey into the wild places beyond.

On my three-and-a-half-hour flight from Moscow, I was fortunate in having as my neighbour a young Russian geological engineer named Mischa who worked at a research station in the middle of the Karakum. He chatted freely about the desert's less predictable qualities and moods. He talked, for example, of its potential fertility. "In the spring, when there are rains," he said, "much of the desert bursts into bloom. It's like that now. Yuri Gagarin, the first astronaut, was surprised to see our deserts green when he orbited over them way back in 1961. That was in April, too. It does not last long, but while it does the deserts are very beautiful. If we could ever find enough water to irrigate them, this country would turn into a garden. There might even be enough water under the desert sands. There are thousands of wells in the desert."

His words seemed to be belied by what I now saw below—barren ground without the slightest sign of human habitation or any vegetation. Mischa looked over my shoulder.

"The Ust Urt," he said, "*Giblaya zemlya*"—the God-forsaken land.

So this was the Ust Urt, probably the most desolate part of Central Asia. Also a desert, but with a difference. There are no sand dunes here, no oases, no desert wells, just dry clay eroded into ridges by wind and flash floods. On the map this was a huge blank area, without a single settlement, a single road, a single wooded spot. It was dotted with salt flats, known in Turkestan as "sors"; and indeed they look from above like malignant sores. This was truly a *giblaya zemlya*.

On the horizon to our left lay a striking feature of this melancholy nothingness: a huge depression known as "Barsa Kel'mes", a Turkmen phrase that means "the place of no return" and is applied to several forbidding areas. It looked like a hole in the ground scooped up by an enormous spoon, its bottom completely covered with white salt.

To reach Ashkhabad from the Ust Urt we had to cross the centre of the Karakum. As we swung south from the Ust Urt the ground was enveloped in a pinkish mist. This, Mischa told me, was a common occurrence, a desert haze caused by strong winds that lifted clouds of fine dust. In the summer, when the sand is driest, this wind causes frequent dust storms—in the Nebit-Dag region, where Mischa worked, they occurred on an average of 60 days each year, blotting out the sun and

*Shells like these are found up to 100 miles away from the Caspian, evidence of how far the water has retreated since the Ice Age ended.*

hindering any work. As we approached Ashkhabad, however, the air cleared enough for us to see, behind the city, the long range of the rolling Kopet-Dag mountains, with their green flanks and snow-patched peaks.

In Ashkhabad I met for the first time my colleagues who were to accompany me throughout the adventure that lay ahead. My closest collaborators were Lev Ustinov, the photographer and Arkady Semonian, a young journalist who was capable of coping with all bureaucratic difficulties large or small.

My objective was to get into the desert itself. I sought the advice of a local expert, Mr. Pavel Ionov. He smiled at my inexperienced request for guidance. "Cross the railway tracks over there," he said, "and in 20 minutes you will be in the Karakum desert." I did as he suggested that afternoon, but my little pilgrimage was not a success. The flat lands beyond the railway tracks were, as Mischa had warned me, a rich green and filled with flowers. This was not exactly what I was after.

When I returned disappointed to Mr. Ionov's office the following morning he laughed at me. To really understand the desert, he explained, I should start from a more desolate area, near a bay known as the Kara-Bogaz-Gol, which bulges out of the Caspian Sea on the desert's western rim. This, he promised, would dramatize the way in which Turkestan's hot, dry air blots up the moisture. I should move on from there into the realm of the sandy desert proper. "But there is little use studying our desert lands," he said, "if you do not try to understand, too, how they have been shaped. You must grasp the importance of water: study its paths and its sources, see where it has an effect and where it does not. Why not travel from west to east, across the desert to the Amu Darya, and then trace the source of all our water into the foothills and the high mountains?" It seemed an inviting plan, and soon afterwards I left for Krasnovodsk on the shores of the Caspian, the first stage in my journey to the Kara-Bogaz-Gol.

The Kara-Bogaz is one of the world's most extraordinary phenomena, a bay of apparently infinite capacity, into which the Caspian pours endlessly through a small neck of water. The surface of the bay, which is 90 miles across and juts out of the Caspian like a giant hernia, lies 13 feet below that of its parent sea. As a result, the water gushes from the Caspian into the bay forming what must be the only salt-water rapids in the world. The Kara-Bogaz (its name means "The Black Maw") is a great cauldron: set in a scorched land of sand, salt and rocks, it boils off the water faster than the Caspian can supply it.

*A furry seal pup lies in the sun on the lake shore. Though there are several hundred seals in the Caspian, how they got to this inland sea—remote from any seal-breeding ground—remains a mystery. It seems probable that the seal came from the Arctic Ocean via rivers such as the prehistoric Volga perhaps as long as a million years ago.*

According to local Turkmen legend, Allah laid a curse upon the Caspian for parting company with her husband, the Black Sea. Allah decreed that their offspring, the Kara-Bogaz, would never cut its umbilical cord with its mother; and so the Caspian would have to feed it with water to the end of time. This natural oddity has fascinated scientists from the day of its discovery in the mid-19th Century. I was eager to see it for myself.

On our arrival at Krasnovodsk I hired a jeep and asked the driver and my guide to head straight for the Kara-Bogaz, 80 miles north. Our road passed through the most desolate part of the Turkmenistan wilderness, the "Land of the Black Maw". The area has a grisly incident in its history: in 1920, during the civil war following the Bolshevik revolution, a group of 300 Red Army prisoners was abandoned at the Kara-Bogaz by their White Army captors and set out to walk to Krasnovodsk. Only two made it; the rest, overcome by the scorching summer gales that whip in from the Karakum, died of heat-stroke. Even cars do not last long in these conditions. "The devil dust gets into the motor and grinds it to pieces," my driver, Ahmed, complained.

Northwards from Krasnovodsk, not a single patch of green breaks the monotony of grey hills and depressions that form the Caspian's coastal strip. The soil is too salty for plant-life and no stream interrupts the surrealistic patterns of salt flats dotting the barren earth. All this is evidence of how the Caspian has continued to shrink since parting company with her "husband": even the vast inflow of the Volga is unable to keep up with the combined effects of evaporation from the Caspian itself and the Kara-Bogaz.

The bay itself is a forbidding sight. As our jeep climbed slowly up a sandy hill, a strangely pre-historic vista opened before us—an enormous lagoon surrounded by bare black hills that jut sharply up to 1,000 feet; around the water's edge was a ribbon of brilliant white that looked like snow; in fact it was an expanse of mirabilite, or sodium sulphate, which the waters of the bay deposit in evaporation. The whole panorama had the strangely haunting beauty of a dead region.

This was no illusion: the water's 35 per cent mineral content is lethal to most forms of life. The effect this place has on visitors was graphically described by the first man to explore the Kara-Bogaz, a Russian naval officer named Ignati Zherebtsov, who in 1847 sailed into the bay to chart it. He later recounted his impressions of "this terrifying crucible" in a letter to a friend. "We sailed," he wrote, "along the shores of the Caspian, against a southern wind bringing from the deserts dust and the smell of sulphur. I had a sweetish taste in my mouth and my sailors spat

Chemical-rich scum flecks the shores of the Kara-Bogaz-Gol (above, foreground), while water pours unceasingly into the foamy bay from its parent, the Caspian Sea, through a 100-yard wide channel (background). Together the bay and the channel form a unique phenomenon. The shallow bay acts as a boiler: extreme evaporation depresses its water level several feet below that of the Caspian—hence the continuous inrush —and also increases its highly concentrated mineral content.

In the shallow, rocky channel—known as the Bitter River—that connects the Caspian and the Kara-Bogaz-Gol, the slate-blue waters form small rapids (right) that swell to cascades during the summer months when evaporation is at its peak and the level of the Kara-Bogaz waters is therefore at its lowest. Formerly an open gulf freely circulating with the Caspian Sea, the bay became separated from its parent by the growth of alluvial sandbars, and these still contribute to its choppiness.

so much that my bosun was in despair. There is an old superstition forbidding sailors to spit overboard in order not to insult the sea and thus risk making it angry. As a result, the deck became covered with spittle and had to be hosed down three times a day.

"We sailed to the Kara-Bogaz in uneasiness and alarm.... Approaching the Kara-Bogaz we saw over the sands a cupola of reddish mist [the dust haze I had seen on my flight to Ashkhabad] as if some immense fire was burning in the desert.... Carried by the current, we swept into the lead-coloured water of the bay, and dropped anchor towards dusk.

"A tremendous silence hung over the place. It seemed that every sound was absorbed by the thick water and the heavy desert air, coloured like blood by the setting sun.... Our cook, a man of little brain, tried to swim, but the bay refused to accept him. It kept throwing his legs up, and he could not go under. This cheered up the crew.

"The next morning," Zherebtsov reported, "the whole bay revealed itself in all its monotony. The water was opaque. Fish, sucked in from the Caspian, were floating about, killed by the saltiness of the water.... Even a short stay in the Kara-Bogaz evokes in one the feeling of utter loneliness and longing for green and inhabited places. Only salt, sands and all killing heat reign over these inhospitable shores and waters."

Three mysteries in particular perplexed Zherebtsov. In the first place, he wondered what happened to the water that swirled into the bay from the Caspian; although he correctly described the bay as a "giant boiler", he wrongly concluded that the water must also drain off through an underground river. Secondly, he was surprised to discover that the salt deposited around the bay was poisonous. When the ship's cook used it to season borsch, the entire crew came down with acute diarrhoea that almost killed them. Finally, he was baffled by the fact that during the winter a coat of white salt covered the surface of the bay, while in the spring it disappeared as if by magic.

Today the questions that puzzled Zherebtsov have been answered. There is no underground river; the water escapes solely by evaporation. Secondly, the salt deposits on the shore of the bay are not palatable sodium chloride but noxious sodium sulphate. And as for the mystery of the disappearing salt: the sodium sulphate—now much prized for industrial purposes—crystallizes when the water's temperature falls below 42° F. and dissolves again when the warm spring weather arrives.

The place is still oppressive. I smelled no sulphur, but the air seemed heavy, and a haze hung over the lead-coloured water. I wanted to drive around the lake but Ahmed, the driver, protested: "That white poison would eat up my tyres. Let's go away from this evil place." I had not come all this way just to stand on the shore, however. I insisted at least on seeing the mouth of the maw, the Adji Darya, the "bitter river" where the Caspian poured into the bay. Grudgingly, Ahmed agreed; we swung westward and north, across the sombre salt flats until the land ended at the entrance to the Kara-Bogaz. Large flocks of seagulls circled at the end of the strait where it reaches the Kara-Bogaz, searching for the fish that are sucked in from the Caspian and killed by the bitter waters (whose salts were clearly not harmful to these hardy birds).

The "bitter river" was a curious sight: the ground is completely flat, and the torrent—about 100 yards across at the nearest point—roars over it as if it was falling down a steep, smooth gradient. It looked like a horizontal waterfall. "P'yanaya voda," Ahmed commented, "the drunken water. But this is just the low water flow. You should come here in July or August. Then the water rushes so fast that it looks like a line of waterfalls. It is like nothing else in the world. Now let's get out of here."

We headed back for Krasnovodsk for a night's rest before going in by rail along the desert's rim back to Ashkhabad. On the way I saw a spectacle that hinted at the desolation that lay to the east. About 100 miles south-east of Krasnovodsk the railway passes two huge outcroppings of rock rising from the desert floor—the Great and Little Balkhan mountains. For me this grotesque chaos of rock, shaped over the centuries by the elements, was—even more than Ashkhabad—the "gateway to the desert", a forbidding foretaste of the wilderness to come.

# The Place of No Return

Two stark mountain ranges, the Great and the Little Balkhans, erupt like gigantic bubbles from the floor of the vast Karakum desert, 75 miles to the east of the Caspian Sea. These masses of rock, sand, mud and other natural debris form desolate landscapes uninhabited by fauna and dotted by only occasional hardy plants. The centre of this area is so barren and its temperatures so extreme ($-25°$ to $+130°$F.) that the Turkmens call it "Barsa Kel'mes"— the place of no return.

As dead and isolated as this western edge of the desert may seem, many natural forces are still alive within it, shifting the arid wilderness in startling and picturesque ways. Mud volcanoes and earthquakes play an active part in the continuing changes. But the single most important process of transformation has been —and continues to be—erosion.

Ironically, it is water—so scarce that, according to a local saying "a waterdrop is a diamond"—which has shaped most of the desert rocks into valleys and hills, and has crisscrossed their stark surfaces with boldly etched patterns. Although the rainfall here is minute, averaging less than six inches annually, the surfaces everywhere are so exposed and so malleable that less than an inch of rain can set into motion the chemical and physical processes by which gullies are carved, loose rock flushed away and holes bored into the hard desert veneer.

Erosion on the Karakum is also aided by the wind, the extreme aridity of the air—and salt. Some salt blows across the desert from the Caspian Sea, coating vast areas with fine crystals. The rest is drawn to the surface of the desert floor through capillary action. In the intensely dry atmosphere the salt dries out in the top layers of the rock and sand, forming soils of especially low fertility. Without plants to bind it, the soil crumbles and becomes prey to the erosive action of the wind. The loose debris picked up by the wind becomes a potent scouring agent, smoothing irregular surfaces into rounded ridges and flat plateaux.

Like the rest of the Soviet Central Asian desert lands, the Karakum is still an active tectonic area. Among the most startling thermal phenomena are mud craters containing large deposits of oil-sand and boiling oxidized pools that seep from under the cracking rocks to spew their rusty coloured liquids over the bleak, grey land.

*As desolate and dramatic as a lunar landscape, this area near the Great Balkhans is called the "Boya-Dag"—or Colourful Mountains—in Turkmen. During the spring storms, water has scarred the grey limestone surfaces, carving out deep gullies and pitting the pebbly shale in the foreground. The dark flame-shaped ridge and the small flat-topped hill in the right background are fragmented peaks of crumpled strata, remnants of the mountain-building activity that formed this wasteland.*

A jagged hole in the Boya-Dag, one of the remotest parts of the Karakum desert, has been created by a hot thermal spring bubbling just beneath the rocky surface. Water erupting like lava from many such mini-caves speckles the crust around the opening with iron oxide, smearing it with colour before causing it to flake away. The water is useless, too hot, acrid, and salty for either drinking or irrigation.

Tear-shaped pools in the Great Balkhans—highly mineralized, hot springs—signal an area of thermal activity and indicate the presence of natural oil and gas far beneath the desert floor. The moisture, known as meteoric water, comes from inside the earth, erupting and disappearing back into the ground in the same spot. Its deep rusty hue comes from its high iron oxide content. The pool is rimmed with deposits of salt which crystallize around its edge. The layers of rock to the left of the hot spring have been scalloped by wind erosion.

*The horizontal bands of white shale and brown sandstone on a desert hill are traversed by a pattern of water gullies like the veins in a leaf.*

*Amoeba-like rocks in a dry river-bed have been polished smooth by high winds carrying bits of loose debris and fine abrasive desert sand.*

This loaf-shaped mountain of sedimentary rock is an awesome example of erosion. The topmost part was once the level bed of a vast inland sea; but the surrounding rock has been ground down over many millennia. The river which eroded the rock is now little more than a seasonally active stream, whose dry bed curls around the bottom of the rock. The stream bed leads to a rarely active waterfall and a "swallow hole", where the water disappears into the ground.

*These conical-shaped holes were gradually created by water dissolving its way into weak spots in the limestone rock and then evaporating.*

*Pinnacles of limestone—ancient strata thrust upright by the earth's mountain-building movements—have been pocked by water and sand.*

This science-fiction scene is actually a wrinkled sea of folded and eroded sedimentary strata whose rock layers were crumpled together about 50 million years ago when the Indian and Asian land masses collided. Since then they have been carved and changed by the continuous forces of desert erosion. The seemingly snow-capped peaks are mantles of salt that have crystallized on the terraced beds of shale. The sharp ridges and the smooth, streaked plateaux were first carved by water and then sculpted by the wind into this starkly beautiful landscape.

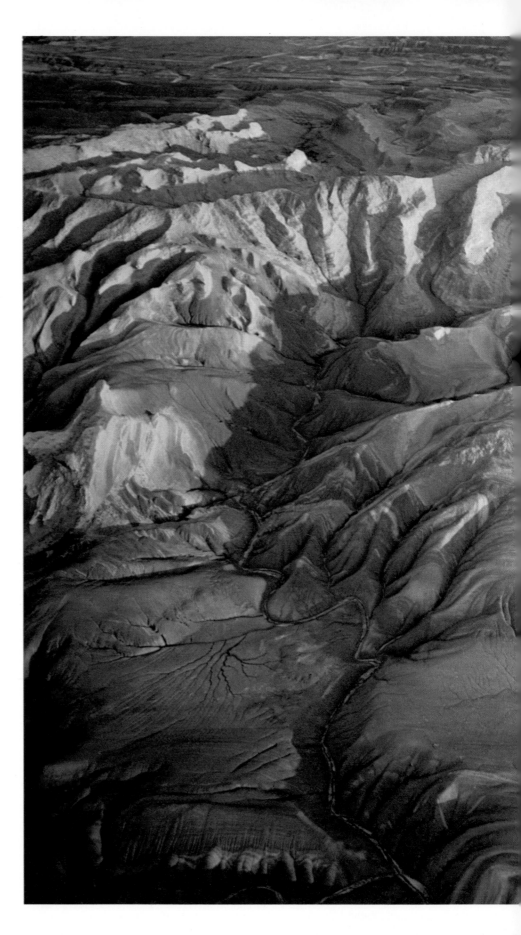

# 2/ On the Edge of Existence

*As I wander out in the gentle spring*
*I hear a keen call of your roads, O Desert!*
*I shall leave my home in the dreary hills*
*How sad are other lands compared to you, O Desert!*

SEIDI (19TH-CENTURY TURKMEN POET)

Millenia have passed since Turkestan was an inland sea, yet a sense of that primeval geography lingers there today. The towns are placed as if they were ports along a coastline. The vast heartland of the Karakum and Kyzylkum deserts remains a great void, left almost empty as if the people were landsmen afraid to put out from the desert's edge. Indeed, the shifting sands and eroding wilderness of these deserts are like a sea, constantly changing and unpredictable, especially at night. To the nomadic Turkmen shepherds who alone wander this wasteland, the one stable point in the ocean of sands is the pole star, just as it is to sailors. They call it *temir bazik*, the iron peg.

At first I found this sandy uniformity of waves and ripples throughly alarming. How does one describe something with a star as one's only point of reference? How could I get to know an area of a quarter of a million square miles?

"So you want to discover our deserts!" replied Professor Anwer Rustamov when I put the question to him. Rustamov, who is president of the Turkmenistan Nature Protection Society in Ashkhabad, probably knows more about the Turkestan deserts and their flora and fauna than anyone else. "One way of doing it is to buy a camel and to cross and recross our country. In 20 years you will have seen a good deal of it." (Rustamov is blessed with a sense of humour nearly as dry as the desert.) "But there is another way. You can visit certain uniquely representative places. I will tell you where to go to see the desert as it is, to see desert forests, shifting sand dunes, plants and animals which have adapted themselves to intense heat and extreme aridity. Life, one might say, at the very edge of existence."

The edge of existence! I could almost feel the hot blast of the desert. An awesome mirage came to my mind's eye: sand dunes stretching to the horizon like waves suddenly frozen in their onrush, bare rocks shimmering in the sun's glare, men dying of thirst and heat. It was a false vision, of course, for life does exist in this wasteland—a reality I still had to grasp. My first task was to understand just how harsh the desert conditions are and to discover how plants and animals can survive there. Then, following Rustamov's advice, I would "see the desert as it is".

Turkestan's deserts are so dry that the mere contemplation of them is enough to parch one's throat. The extreme aridity is a direct result of the country's geographical position in the centre of a great land mass thousands of miles from any ocean. Moisture carried from the Atlantic on the world's prevailing westerly winds falls as rain and snow long before reaching central Turkestan. Any air coming from the south is about as dry as air can be. Because of the great heat at the equator, air rises in convection currents that turn outwards to north and south, and as it meets the colder temperatures of the upper air, it loses its moisture through condensation and rainfall. The northerly winds sweeping down from Siberia have covered such great distances over dry land that they bring only a little moisture.

So the Turkestan deserts receive scarcely any rain. And the little that does arrive descends in a few days in winter or spring. It never amounts to more than ten inches a year, and in some areas only a fraction of that. Droughts as long as ten years have been recorded. Turkestan lies on the same latitude as Lisbon and San Francisco—38° N—and is exposed to long hours of sunlight, which also does its part to wring any moisture out of the air. Moist air is essential for an equable climate, since it filters the direct heat of the sun by day and helps retain the heat by night. Lack of moisture creates a climate of violent extremes. So in moisture-starved Turkestan, the desert receives the full force of the sun during the day, and loses its heat rapidly as soon as the sun goes down. In July and August the midday air temperature may hit 120° F. The sand and rocks are heated to about 180° F. As night comes on, the mercury drops dramatically. Falls of as much as 80° between noon and midnight have been recorded—from 120° F down to 40° F. In southern parts of the deserts, winters are short but cold, with occasional light falls of snow and tem-

A buff-coloured toadstool (above) casts its shadow on the desert sand in the wake of a spattering of rain. Underground the toadstool's mycelium of thread-like filaments reaches out to a buried grass root (marked by the sand-ridge, right), from which the fungus derives its food.

Rosettes of tiny leaves protrude through a cloak of sand soon after the germination of a desert-hardy strand plant. The rosettes, which are off-shoots of a single plant, are linked underground by a network of roots that drink up any available moisture, storing it for drier months.

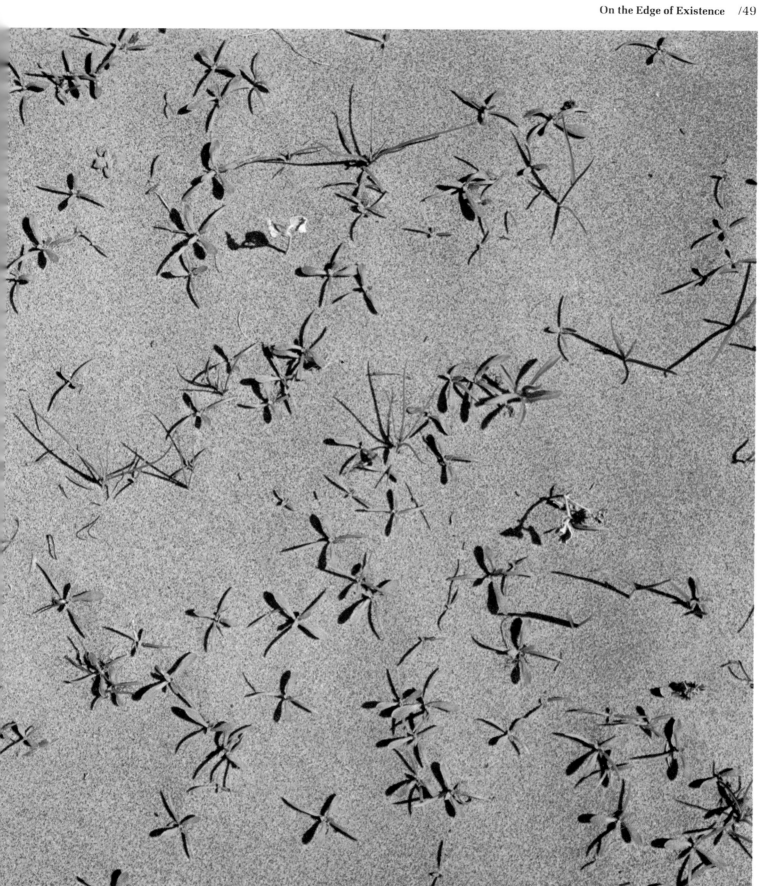

peratures below freezing during cold spells. Farther north, the conditions are more severe; the Aral Sea, at the northern tip of the Karakum desert, freezes over for four or five months of the year.

During the long, hot summers, the little rain that falls evaporates immediately. Even an enormous increase in the rainfall would not be enough to keep the soil moist. Whatever the potential fertility of the soil laid down at the end of the Ice Age, such conditions turn it to desert.

This extreme aridity has a further effect on large areas of the desert: salts are drawn up to the surface by capillary action, preventing the formation of humus. Without water and without humus, plants cannot take root. And without plants to bind it, the soil becomes prey to the erosive action of the wind that sweeps over the desert at speeds of up to 90 m.p.h. So the soil in these areas is whipped up and whirled away, and turned by the wind into a powerful scouring agent which sandblasts the landscape, until rock formations become rounded or fretted. Loose sand piles up into desert waves, the frightening *barchans*, or crescent-shaped dunes of shifting sands.

In planning my expedition into the great void, I first considered going to the Kyzylkum. Lying to the north-east of the Amu Darya river, it is the smaller of the two deserts, occupying about 78,000 square miles. It contains a complex and varied mosaic of landscapes. There are mountain areas that were once islands in Turkestan's inland sea—now surfaced with stones. There are foothill plateaux topped with a mixture of sand and gravel. And there are plains covered with the red sand from which the Kyzylkum takes its name (*kyzyl*, meaning red, and *kum* meaning sands). This sand was brought down from the mountains during the Ice Age when a higher rainfall and lower evaporation made the ancient rivers much more swollen than they are today. But to me the Kyzylkum's variety of landscape was a positive disadvantage. I wanted to see the desert at its most extreme.

Accordingly, I decided to concentrate on the Karakum, Turkestan's true desert heart. The so-called Black Sands of the Karakum span the whole enormous area of 188,500 square miles between the Caspian Sea and the Amu Darya. Three-quarters of it is sand—loose sands, sand hills and shifting dunes—and there is only one obvious break in the forbidding expanse. This is the barren Zaunguzk Plateau lying some 200 feet above the mean level of the Karakum. It is a sort of "first floor"—without stairs, for it ends with a sheer drop at its southern edge. The other two-thirds of the desert are known simply and austerely as the south-eastern and central Karakum.

Like those of the Kyzylkum, the sands of the Karakum were also brought down by rivers—chiefly the Amu Darya—from the mountains, and deep beneath the surface lie beds of rich soil exactly like the alluvium the river is bringing down today. Around the edges of the Karakum there are also surface remnants of this ancient silt, which was blown off the desert as a fine dust in ages past and settled to form loess soils. This may explain why the sands are called black, even though they do not appear so. In contemporary Turkmen the word *karakum* is applied to parts of the desert that have some grass cover, to distinguish them from the *ak-kum*, or white sands, which are lifeless. *Kara*, whose first meaning is "black", may also signify fertile, as in "black earth", because for a few weeks in the spring, when the brief rains give the ancient silts a chance, large parts of the desert bloom like an English meadow.

I had my first good view of the Karakum from the air, when I flew over its south-eastern edge on a day in late spring when the desert was not shrouded in its customary pinkish haze. Although there was still some green vegetation to be seen, I was more impressed by the areas of total barrenness. There were large patches of yellow—probably loose sands. I also noticed some peculiar brown spots, perfectly smooth and mostly circular, some small and some quite large; these were *takyrs*, clay patches that are moisture-proof and support no vegetation apart from lichens and algae. Some of them cover hundreds of square miles and create what is known locally as "clay desert". *Takyrs* are formed by temporary spring streams flowing into depressions or flat stretches. Quickly evaporating under the sun, the water leaves behind deposits of clay, which over the centuries build up into a hard surface. Under the constant brushing of wind-borne sand, this becomes as highly polished as the top of a piano, and in storms the sand waves glide over them as easily as if they were on ice.

Later in the flight I came to a truly desolate landscape: ridge upon ridge of corrugated dunes, entirely devoid of vegetation. The sun had dried all traces of the spring rains here. Along the tops of crescent-shaped dunes the desert wind caught up the fine sand and whipped it into plumes that rose in the air like strands of vapour from dormant volcanoes. These were *barchans*, the ocean waves of the desert. As the winds winnow off the crests and toss the sandy chaff down into the troughs, the *barchans* gradually move forward, travelling as much as 100 feet a year in particularly windy areas. Although they cover only 17.2 million acres or about ten per cent of the Karakum, they make up for their comparatively small extent in sheer destructiveness.

When a strategic railway was built across the southern Karakum in 1880, it was hailed as an outstanding engineering feat. But it proved almost impossible to operate. The shifting sands constantly threatened to swallow it, and every train had to carry a team of workers to clear the line. The newspaper *Askabad*, as Ashkhabad was then spelled, spoke with alarm of a "terrible sand siege" and prophesied the "eventual destruction" of the railway. This might indeed have occurred, had not trees and shrubs been planted and nurtured to anchor the *barchans*.

Looking down on mile upon mile of this desolate country, I could understand why the few European explorers who have braved it considered it unutterably hostile. Arminius Vambery, a Hungarian explorer who crossed the Karakum in the 19th Century, recalled how he was unable to discover "the slightest trace of a path indicated by foot of camel or other animal . . . how this eternal sadness of the plain, from which every trace of life is banished, wearies the traveller," he wrote. A similar sentiment was expressed by an English visitor, Alexander Burnes: "All other deserts are insignificant in comparison to this endless ocean of sands. I cannot imagine a sight more terrible".

That is how the desert strikes outsiders. Yet the nomads—the Tekins, the Salars, the Ersars, the Iomuds, the Karandashlis—would not live anywhere else. In Turkmen there is a special word to describe them all: *kumli*, "sand people", and they are united by their attitudes as well as their name. "Every time I think about the sunset in the desert," an old Karakum shepherd told me in an Ashkhabad bazaar, "my heart bleeds for these poor people here who have never seen that beauty. Tomorrow, if Allah lets me sell my sheep, I will leave this den of iniquity and confusion and return to the desert splendour, where I shall pray to be permitted to die without ever seeing all this sinful ugliness again."

He was an old man, claiming to be "over 100 as Allah counts the moon", with a snow-white beard cut along the oval of his chin, framing the lower part of his fine sun-scorched face. He wore the usual garb of the *kumli*—a *telpek*, or heavy round hat made of goat fur, a long cotton-lined robe, very wide cotton trousers and brown boots of untanned goat-skin. Already the temperature was around 80° F, and yet he showed no sign of discomfort in his heavy clothing. The *kumli* wear this dress in all seasons. They say it protects them from both the burning sun and the icy winter winds. They should know. They have worn it for centuries.

In the desert the shepherds live to a steady rhythm, constantly on the move with their flocks by day, resting at night around camp fires of *kiziak*, the sheep manure which is their staple fuel. Nomads are a dying breed, but there are still about 25,000 of them in the Karakum, and their quiet existence has on occasion lured Turkmens and Uzbeks away from the comfortable new towns. This life has attracted strangers too—Russians, Ukrainians, Belorussians and others. "Even the young ones go there," my host in Ashkhabad told me. "They are enchanted by the bitter-sweet smell of the *kiziak*, by tales of long ago told at the fireside by the old men, and by the haunting, melancholy songs. The desert tempts them with its horizons, the constant changes of its soft colours, by the calmness of dusk, when the air becomes cold and invigorating, and the myriads of bright stars in the night sky. The sheer poetry gets them."

"But isn't it a hard life?" I asked.

"Yes, but also free and simple. There are few problems, few anxieties."

My host's eulogy may seem odd to outsiders who do not see how anyone or anything could even exist in a desert, let alone prefer such a way of life. But plants, insects, reptiles, mammals and men can survive in the desert, providing they have special methods of coping with the heat and aridity. These adaptations are responsible for the apparent lifelessness of the desert. The plants and animals are there, but to avoid the sun, and to conserve every drop of moisture, they keep themselves out of sight, or take on the aspect of the dead.

One of the eeriest sights of Turkestan is the series of apparently dead forests of shrub-like trees in the south-east Karakum. These consist of two varieties of the saxaul tree: the white, which grows on sandy soil and bears minute leaves, and the black, which grows on more saline soil and has no leaves at all. Both present an appearance of mid-winter leaf-lessness throughout the year. Being bare, or nearly bare, they present less surface area to the arid air around them. The evaporation that in other plants takes place through the leaves is restricted in saxauls to the branches; and the branches, in an additional water-conserving adapta-tion, fall off after the plant has borne fruit.

The saxauls are perhaps the most dramatic case of adaptation to drought, but other types of vegetation in the desert also have some remarkable survival techniques. Most of them are ephemerals, living a brief life for five or six weeks in spring and lapsing into inactivity for the rest of the year. To take full advantage of the wet season, their life cycle has speeded up: they seize upon moisture and pass through all their stages of development, up to the formation of seeds, before the dry season begins. This truncated existence accounts for the astonishing

*These apparently dead white saxaul trees have only temporarily shed their tiny leaves to conserve moisture during the long, dry summer.*

transformation of the southern Karakum when the surface, barren at other times of the year, bursts into bloom.

Another characteristic type of desert vegetation in Turkestan is the psammophilic, or sand-loving, plant, capable of living in loose sands. The sand acacia, for example, has roots 50 feet long or more, which reach down to the sub-soil waters and sustain it through the summer. Other plants spread their roots horizontally and gather the last drops of moisture from the upper layers of sand. All these psammophilic plants have tiny leaves to reduce water loss to a minimum.

The specialized plants of the desert provide the life-giving basis for a restricted range of animals, also skilfully adapted to life at the edge of existence. The plants serve two vital functions for these creatures: binding the sand together, so that an animal may dig a safe burrow, and providing food. Yet such is the paucity of vegetation, and so extreme the conditions of aridity and heat, that the most successful animals are either especially well adapted to desert conditions (the cold-blooded reptiles) or small enough to need little food or space for shelter. In the Karakum these small creatures are chiefly insects, of which over 10,000 species have been identified, and rodents, such as sand rats, gerbils and susliks, far-flung relatives of the familiar American ground squirrels. These plant-eating animals are preyed upon by legions of lizards and snakes. At the top of the food chain are a few predatory birds, high-flying desert hawks which take all the moisture they need from the blood of their prey.

None of the desert creatures can stand extreme heat, so they simply avoid it: most of the animal life in the Karakum desert takes place under-ground. Rodents dig burrows and retreat in the heat of the day into their own micro-climates where humidity can be up to five times as great as outside and the temperature is a great deal lower. The roots of desert plants provide them with food. Snakes make use of the burrows as well, perhaps eating the rodent occupants.

Other reptiles, notably the lizards, scuttle into the loose sand; even a few inches down, it is much cooler than on the surface. Some insects raise themselves off the scorching sand surface on long spindly legs or, like the locust, simply fly over it. The desert tortoises, on the other hand, escape the heat by season instead of by day or night. They are active only in spring and spend the entire period from the end of May to the follow-ing April in burrows in summer "hibernation", or what zoologists call aestivation (from *aestes*, the Latin for summer).

*A tree locust—a member of a sedentary, non-swarming species—rests on a desert rock, discreetly camouflaged from its many predators.*

For most desert creatures, evening is the time for action. As the sun goes down, the temperature begins to drop, and everything which walks, runs, burrows, slithers and flies comes to life. Even then it is not easy to spot anything, for many desert creatures are well camouflaged against the sand. Agamid lizards have even evolved a signalling device so that their own kind can see them. On the underside of the tail they have broad criss-crossed stripes of bright red and black which stand out strongly against the sand when the tail is lifted and waved in a sort of lizard semaphore. Occasionally at dusk, one can see, on the bare slope of a sand dune, a group of agamid lizards, their colours standing out like flags on a military map, spiralling up and down the slope. At the first sign of danger, they lower their tail flags and vanish instantly into their sandy camouflage. If they suspect that an intruding predator such as a bird of prey is about to give chase they will suddenly part the sand beneath them with swift sideways movements of their bellies and disappear, leaving only a tiny ripple in the desert.

The problem of finding and conserving water in the Karakum has been solved in a number of ingenious ways. Some creatures have learned to store moisture in their bodies, usually in the form of fat which later breaks up and turns into what is known as "metabolic water". Many rodents get all the liquid they need from the juicy roots of desert plants, and gerbils are so economical in their use of water that they excrete balls of almost dry dust. Another advantage possessed by desert animals is the ability to drink water with such a high salt content that other animals, including man, would be unable to stomach it.

Among these salt water-drinking animals are the camel and sheep, which provide the only livelihood for the desert nomads. These animals can find enough food for grazing from the scant grass cover, even when it has become withered and burnt by the sun. The camels have the added ability to eat alhagi shrubs, the "camel prickle" that is too tough for sheep or other animals to digest. In the Karakum camels are irreplaceable as beasts of burden and also as a source of food. But the sheep are more important still. Not only do they provide mutton (with a peculiar but not unpleasant flavour), they also yield fur; the karakul sheep produce the Persian lamb fur that is so highly valued in world markets.

The most common karakul fur is jet black, but there are innumerable varieties ranging from black to golden-yellow, the rarest and most valuable. Occasionally the golden-fleeced lambs are born with a temporary luminous glow on their coats. Local people call them "fire lambs", and believe that they bring good luck to the ewe's owners. When I was in

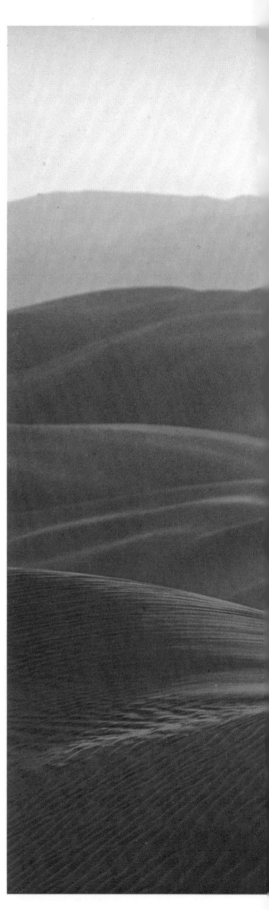

Guided by antennae, a darkling beetle
makes hurried tracks across the sand,
scavenging for minute quantities of
plant and animal matter, or possibly for
the larvae of other insects. Its compact
shape and thick shell cut down the
evaporation of body fluids, while the
white stripes break up its black outline
and help conceal it from predators.

Desert tortoises make a laborious—and
apparently fruitless—springtime foray
for food from their oasis home, which
lies out of sight in the dip behind them.
In the brief eight to ten weeks of spring,
they store food and water, mate and
breed before retiring to burrows in
which to sleep through the extreme
summer and winter temperatures.

Tashkent during the final stages of my journey through Turkestan, a young woman journalist told me she had once seen a fire-lamb in Karakalpakia (*karakalpak* means "black hat", the normal headwear of the local Uzbek inhabitants).

"I was awakened one night," she recalled, "by the sound of many excited voices and footsteps outside. Somebody knocked at my door: 'Come and see a strange new-born lamb! Even its own mother is afraid of it!' When I entered a dark shack, I stood there dumbfounded. I had never seen anything like it before. On the hay in the corner lay the lamb, and its still wet coat was glowing in the dark! Actually glowing—there was no light it could reflect. The ewe was lying some distance away, looking at her offspring from the corners of her eyes. As I stood there the glow started to decrease in intensity, and in about five minutes it was gone. Someone brought in an oil lantern and we saw the lamb had a gold-coloured fleece. People were babbling excitedly. Apparently a fire-lamb had not been born for 20 years in Karakalpakia. The old woman who owned the sheep could not say a word; she was crying almost hysterically out of sheer happiness."

I asked the girl if she had any idea how the effect was created. Could the cause be luminous bacteria? Probably, but she could not say for certain. She told me that several fire-lambs are said to be born in Turkestan every year, but up to the night when she saw this one, she had always dismissed the reports. Being less sceptical, I believed her story.

For the shepherds who wander the Karakum with their flocks, the chief problem is finding drinkable water. They base themselves near one or more of the 20,000 wells that are scattered across the Karakum. Close to the Amu Darya these wells may be only 10 to 20 feet deep, but farther away from the river they reach down 100 to 250 feet, and occasionally 1,000 feet or more. Many yield only a few gallons of water a day, and others are seasonal, almost drying up in summer. In low-lying areas, water can sometimes be found quite close to the surface, as little as 5 to 15 feet down. The only other source of water comes from the atmosphere. Spring and autumn rains and fitful winter snowfalls provide only a meagre amount, but the *kumli* have developed many ingenious ways of preserving this precious liquid. They scoop it out from concave *takyrs*, the non-porous clay basins in the desert, and store it in deep holes lined with stone. These storage pits are topped off by vaulted stone lids resembling machine-gun emplacements. These *sardobas*, as they are known, can be found all over the desert. In northern Karakum, they are packed with snow in winter and provide the local people with enough fresh water for drinking through the summer.

After my first meeting with Professor Rustamov, I completed part one of my plan: I studied all the details of the Karakum and its inhabitants, beginning with the psammophilic plants and going up through insects, rodents, reptiles, sheep and camels to the *kumli*. When I next saw Rustamov, I was ready to take up his offer to point out a representative part of the desert to visit.

"You must go to Repetek," he said. I had to confess I had never heard of the place.

"Well, it's a particularly wild and drought-ridden part of the southeast Karakum. Down there, they have *barchans*, saxaul forests and many of the distinctive fauna of Turkestan. Best of all, from your point of view, the area is a nature reserve with a desert research station, and I am sure that one of the scientific staff will take you around."

Back at the hotel I spread out my map of Turkestan. There was Repetek, situated on the railway line linking Ashkhabad with Chardzhou, the second largest city of Turkmenia. It was Friday, and Ashkhabad is not an entertaining place to spend the weekend. Why not use the time to see Repetek?

# The Wind-Shaped Sands

"It has all the appearance of a sea of troubled waves, billow succeeding billow in melancholy succession, with the sand driving like spray from their summits, and great smooth-swept troughs lying in between." This was how Lord Curzon, future Viceroy of India, described the Karakum desert when he crossed it in 1889. Curzon's poetic analogy is completely accurate. The loose sand —which comprises no more than 10 per cent of the desert—moves much like the sea, changing with the wind and rippling in the softest breeze. But the desert, unlike waves, preserves the trace of winds in its sand formations that are classified into three types, according to size.

The smallest formations in the desert are ripples only an inch or two high and spaced a few inches apart. When the wind blows across the desert, it picks up sand grains, bouncing them along the surface. The bouncing grains dislodge coarser sand grains, too heavy for the wind, and nudge them along.

If these encounter a chance irregularity, they pile up until they reach a height at which any additional sand is moved over the top of the new ripple; this process continues across the desert until a new wind changes the direction of the ripples.

The second type of sand formation is the small dune, often six feet or so high. These dunes are thought to reflect wave-like flow in the wind. Between the waves, where the speed of the wind drops, the blown sand accumulates to form a dune.

Immense dunes, commonly 300 feet high and sometimes as much as 1,000, make up the largest sand formations. These are formed by the same flow in the wind as their smaller counterparts, but at a much greater scale. Such features reflect the wind patterns of centuries.

If the winds blew constantly and always from the same direction, these ripples and waves would form a regular, if complex pattern. In fact, the desert winds change direction and speed and are deflected by the very sand formations they have sculpted. It is these irregularities in the wind patterns that continually rewrite the sand into undulating curves, twists and whorls. In the pictures on the following pages, taken in the Karakum and Kyzylkum deserts, lying between the Caspian Sea and the Pamir and Tien Shan mountains, each pattern in the sand reveals what sort of winds have blown across the desert surface.

*The sands of the Karakum roll into the distance, moulded by the wind into the desert's three main configurations. In the foreground, ripples a few inches high indent a three-foot dune, while in the middle and far background ripples and small dunes are superimposed on the sides of giant dunes that are, on average, some 300 feet in height.*

Ripples spread across the desert in an even and uninterrupted pattern. The wind has blown from left to right, as shown by the nearly vertical drop on the right of each ripple. It takes no more than a few hours to form such ripples, but those pictured below are well set, indicating that the wind has probably not changed for days.

An irregular sand pattern reveals the complex relationship between wind-flow and sand formations. The predominant wind, from right to left, has made the ripples that run back from the foreground. But a dune, left of centre, has deflected the wind around it, and the resulting eddy has shaped the horizontal ripples behind the dune's crest.

Changing wind patterns have moulded these elegant variations of sand. An undulating current has shaped the dunes, but sinuous eddies in the wind have given them their serpentine form. The prevailing wind has come from the left, but changed before the dune pattern was complete. The new wind, its direction indicated by the oblique ripples in the sand and the crimping on the crest of the dune, has already begun its levelling process.

The soft outlines of these crestless dunes show the effect of a 180-degree change in the wind direction. Evidently the winds are seasonal: thus one wind came from left to right for several months, building up dunes that an opposite wind began to remould over the following months, leaving these smooth undulations in the sand.

Two clumps of camel-hair brush, acting
as wind deflectors, stand amidst
their own miniature environment of
swirling sand. The prevailing wind has
been slowed within the clumps of grass,
allowing sand to pile up at root level.
The curving ripple patterns reflect the
way in which the wind has been
deflected around the clumps, and the
edges of the sand hill mark the farthest
extent of the disturbance. The tiny
ripples (right foreground), running at
right angles to the main ones, are a
result of the most recent wind changes:
a gentle wind from a new direction
replaced the stronger one which
formed the main ripple system.

# 3/ The Desert in Miniature

*The desert is warm as a prayer and dry as a curse.*

*TURKMEN PROVERB*

Being a foreigner in the Soviet Union has its disadvantages. One must depend on Intourist, the gigantic state tourist organization which is there to watch, guide, protect, transport, lodge, entertain, beguile, nurse and spoon-feed all visitors. So naturally I consulted the Intourist representative in Ashkhabad, a very polite girl. She was most sympathetic. Repetek? Of course it could be arranged, though it might take a few days. But could I not take a train there right now? Well, no. Intourist in Turkmenia never transport foreign tourists by rail, but only in aeroplanes and private cars. A car then? Yes, she was sure she could arrange one for me . . . on Monday, perhaps. But then I was bound to need a permit and that might take a day or two. She would check . . . on Monday.

I am an old hand at travelling in the Soviet Union. I love Intourist. Some of my best friends work for it. I admire their efficiency—considering the scope of the operation. I am deeply grateful to them for their efforts to secure my comfort and safety. But I am also familiar with their ability to conjure up obstacles and thus discourage over-adventurous tourists. So I thanked my charming Intourist wet-nurse and told her not to worry about me. I said I wanted to rest and that I would see her on Monday. I left and took matters into my own hands. As a born Russian who had a thoroughly Russian raincoat and a cotton shirt—bought at the G.U.M. department store in Moscow—I could lose myself for a day by melting into the landscape. I told the floor attendant in my hotel that

I was invited to a wedding and might not be in for one night. The kind lady understood: Turkestan weddings can last for several days and nights. She smiled knowingly and wished me a good time.

Without any baggage and wearing my G.U.M. clothes I walked to the railway station where I bought a round trip ticket to Repetek, a journey of about 200 miles each way. No one asked any questions, and the train pulled out of Ashkhabad late that night.

At about six the next morning I got off at my destination. The little station was deserted, as was the village. The only signs of life were crowing roosters and barking dogs. Light rain had fallen during the night. The air was pleasantly cool and the sky clear. According to the time-table, the train back to Ashkhabad was scheduled at 1300 hours, which actually meant 1500 hours, since the "1300" was Moscow time. (All railway and airline schedules in the Soviet Union show only Moscow time.) I had nine hours.

I looked around. To the right and left of the railway tracks stretched a desert landscape of undulating sand hills dotted with shrubs. Nearby were several houses surrounded by trees. That, I thought to myself, would be the desert research station. All the windows were shuttered. It was Saturday and the Soviet people take their weekends seriously. I decided to wait a little before going there to ask for a guide. I had thought up my cover story: I can speak Ukrainian pretty well, so I was to be a nature lover from the Ukraine who wanted to take a look at the celebrated establishment.

Suddenly I heard a cracked voice behind my back:

"Don't leave without paying!"

Startled, I turned around. An admission charge? The platform was deserted, but then I saw the source of the voice. It was a large bedraggled mynah bird in a cage hanging near the entrance to the station building. I later learned that several of these birds, which are remarkable talkers (better than parrots) when trained as pets, were brought to Repetek from India during the 1950s. Most of them were released to nest and breed, and they were still flourishing.

"Hassan's a fool!" the bird croaked again. It spoke Russian with a heavy Turkmen (or was it Indian?) accent. An old man, wearing loose pyjama-like clothes and an old faded army cap without any insignia, came out of the station building. Hassan, no doubt. He was barefoot and sported a hanging moustache exactly like the kind worn by Taras Bulba, the fictional Cossack leader. Turning to me and pointing to the bird, he explained: "She was brought up in a tavern."

The man proved to be talkative. He was a Ukrainian from Kharkov and had lived in Turkestan for 50 years. It was all right here, he felt, except for being too hot and dusty in summer. The Ukraine was better. A real garden country, that. Cherry trees were in full bloom there now. Was I a professor? Professors always came here to look at the sand.

"Well, sort of," I said. "From . . . " and hesitated. My Ukraine story might not stand up before someone from the Ukraine. " . . . from Leningrad."

The bird was now whistling *Midnight in Moscow*, badly out of tune. It was a better talker than a whistler.

"You want to see the sand?" the old man asked.

I said yes, but added that I thought I had better see some people at the research station; perhaps they could give me a guide.

"Ostap, my son, knows this place better than those people there," the old man said—and the association with Taras Bulba was completed; Bulba also had a son called Ostap.

"He works at the station, but today is a holiday. He loves to show the sand to people. Ostap, come here!"

Ostap was a strapping lad of perhaps 23, with a handsome, weather-beaten face. He also wore pyjamas which were stuck into heavy boots. On his head was a *tiubiteika* or embroidered skull-cap.

"Here's a famous academician from Leningrad," his father told him in Ukrainian, a language he presumably thought I did not understand. "He wants to see the sand and will pay you for your trouble." So I was upgraded to an academician, the highest Soviet scientific title. "No money," Ostap said. "But the professor had better watch for snakes, seeing that he wears no boots."

Ostap brought out two long strips of burlap and advised me to wrap them around my legs. There were apparently nine varieties of snakes at Repetek though of those only two kinds were really dangerous: the blunt-nosed viper and the carpet or saw-scaled viper. The rest, mostly harmless, included the "arrow snake" and a small sand boa. As I wrapped the burlap around my legs, Ostap gave me a quick resumé of the place. The reserve comprised roughly 86,000 acres and was divided by the railway track into an eastern and western part. The eastern side was twice as large as the other and contained the best black saxaul trees in the Karakum desert.

Ostap was a mine of information. A graduate of Tashkent University where he was a zoology student, he was now working at Repetek as a "junior science collaborator". He was also writing his doctoral disserta-

*A keen-sighted Pleske's ground jay scratches in sand for the insects and seeds that form the bulk of its diet. If it is successful, it will satisfy its appetite and then bury remaining food in a cache to which it will return when alternative supplies run low.*

tion. He intended to return to Tashkent, where he was going to marry and settle down; his bride-to-be was a biochemist.

"Let's start with the black saxaul groves," he suggested.

"Don't leave without paying!" the old mynah bird reminded me.

It was a longish walk along the railway track. After a while we turned left and found ourselves amongst the saxauls, which, according to one Soviet writer, "make a strange and awe-inspiring impression on a person who is not accustomed to them. The black leafless trees have the most fantastic, grotesque appearance resembling mysterious enchanted forests." I thought that this description was somewhat of an exaggeration. It was a singular-looking grove to be sure, but it hardly seemed grotesque. The air was filled with the chirping of birds that fluttered amid the trees and circled overhead.

It was obviously not the first time that Ostap had acted as a guide. His manner was coolly professional and his vocabulary of zoological and botanical names prodigious. The black saxaul (my old friend *Arthrophytum aphyllum*) he told me, was a typical desert tree: leafless to conserve moisture, and with deep roots to probe for water. Unlike the white saxaul which rarely formed groves, the black saxaul usually grew thickly in low ravines, flourishing even in saline soil. These groves have always been quite rare in the desert, and the Repetek ones therefore represented a monument to a bygone era. Here they covered almost 5,000 acres, and were the largest remaining groves on earth.

Black saxauls can grow to a height of 30 feet, but most of these were much shorter. The tall grass around them was sprinkled with ox-eye daisies, red poppies, malcomias, dandelions, blossoming astragal and calligonum bushes, and the grove looked almost festive. "Irises and heliotropes will come out later," Ostap said. "Altogether we have 101 varieties of grass and shrub growing in this grove. But the best way to see it is at night when the moon is out. Then it really looks weird." Many birds nested in the black saxaul groves, he said, but few lived here permanently. Altogether 140 species had been identified at Repetek, but only 40 nested there, and less than 20 stayed more or less permanently.

"That's quite an extraordinary number," Ostap said. "Usually, birds don't live in deserts because they can't burrow into the sand like other creatures. The only true desert bird is the saxaul jay or Pander's chough-thrush, a bird related to the crow family. There are some, look!" There were quite a few of them around: small magpie-like birds with short tails and white ribbons along the edges of their wings.

"Wonderful sand-diggers, they are," Ostap went on. "They dig out insects and seeds from the sand dunes and lay away food stores near the roots of desert shrubs. Since they can't burrow they make their nests in the empty tunnels of various desert rodents where it is cool in summer and warm in winter."

"Now, look at that one," he said in excitement, pointing out a new species. It was a small, inconspicuous grey bird resembling a sparrow.

"Doesn't look like anything, does it? And yet it's the rarest bird we have: the Karakum desert sparrow. In 1926 this bird was declared extinct, yet we still have a few of them around Repetek. They exist nowhere else as far as I know."

For some time now I had been watching some small, screaming birds turning and twisting in a series of brilliant manoeuvres overhead, and I called Ostap's attention to them. "Larks?" Ostap looked up. "Those are 'dancing Kamenkas'," he said. "They are closely related to the crested lark, but they don't call as larks do. They steal their songs from everybody. They imitate not only kites, blackbirds, magpies and shrikes— among others—but also donkeys and camels. Even train whistles. Now it's the mating season and they're going crazy." "Dancing larks" seemed a good name for them, considering their breathtaking acrobatics.

Meanwhile Ostap was rolling off the scientific names of all Repetek's nesting birds. Though I recognized some, this name-dropping business was becoming a bit tiresome and I suggested that we move on. I had still not seen the desert proper. We started to climb a rather high ridge dotted with camel-thorn.

"You know what they call camel-thorn in the desert?" Ostap asked. "Rivets. Their roots go down 100 feet or more into the sand and really nail it down. Of course they're invaluable as camel food, too."

The sandy slope on which we now stood was perforated with hundreds of holes that made it look like a piece of Swiss cheese. "Susliks," Ostap explained. "There are two kinds here: the yellow suslik and the long-toed suslik. Funny little fellows. They sit up on their haunches, like tiny pillars, to see what's going on. Foxes and jackals make short work of them, though. So do the sand cats."

As we walked on, small lizards constantly darted away, while tortoises lazily picked at the blades of grass. Ostap lifted one up and it immediately withdrew into its shell.

"If you want to learn how desert creatures survive, you should study the desert tortoise. In May she will burrow into the sand and go to sleep until next spring. It is amazing how in just eight to ten weeks such a slow

*Ears alert, a desert fox stalks its prey across wasteland turned marshy by recent rains. A large mammal by desert standards, this fox can ill afford to be a fussy eater and applies equal skill and patience to capturing rodents, birds, reptiles and even insects. In summer it is nocturnal, often spending its days in an empty rodent burrow that it has enlarged as refuge from the heat.*

creature manages to mate, lay eggs twice and accumulate enough fat containing all the energy and water she needs to sustain her through the summer and winter. She may wake up for a week or two in the autumn, but she usually sleeps right through. The eggs are laid in May and are incubated until the following spring."

Something else attracted his attention and he put the tortoise down.

"Now watch this," he said. He broke off a twig, dug it into a depression in the sand and flipped over a thick snake, perhaps three feet long, that looked more like a gigantic earthworm. It had a peculiar tail ending abruptly in a sort of stump. It immediately curled up into a tight ball, as though badly scared.

"The sand boa," Ostap said. "Not dangerous to man. Look at its eyes. They're at the top of its head like periscopes. They allow it to crawl under the sand and still look around." After a moment the snake unrolled and moved away quickly; in a few seconds it had buried itself in the sand.

"They eat small tortoises and tortoise eggs," Ostap said, "but they can do nothing with an adult tortoise. They are not strong enough to crush its shell." However there were a few empty and crushed tortoise-shells lying in the sand. Ostap turned one over with his foot.

"One of our giant monitor lizards got these. Some of the monitors are over five feet long. They eat just about everything: other lizards, sand mice, rats. Even their own young. We don't see many of them here. They are becoming rare. People kill them for their skins. To make women's purses. But luckily I have a fine *varan* at home. I'll show you when we get back."

"At home?" I asked, rather puzzled.

"Yes, I've rigged up my own little zoo. You see, since almost all desert creatures here are nocturnal, I've had to pen them up in order to study them at all times."

We were approaching the top of the hill where there were several tall and graceful trees resembling weeping willows. Their short leaves were fluttering in the wind.

"White saxauls?" I ventured a guess.

"No, those are 'sand acacias'," Ostap said. "Very remarkable trees. Excellent sand stoppers. Their roots spread extensively and remain close to the surface in order to collect as much moisture as possible. You will see them all over our deserts—but never in groves. They are lonely fellows and, if you ask me, the most beautiful of all sand-trees."

By this time we had reached the top of the hill. Here we stopped, quite out of breath. The panorama stretching before us was spectacular:

ridge after ridge of sand dunes rolling away as far as the eye could see. Viewed on the ground, they were far more awe-inspiring than from the air. It was like being far out at sea in a dinghy.

"This is our 'backyard of hell'," he said. "It's the piece of the desert with the deadliest type of shifting sands. Here at Repetek they travel up to 50 feet per year: half a year in one direction and half a year in another. We do nothing to stop them since this is our laboratory. We study their behaviour, calculate their dynamics, develop ways of controlling them. On the loose they can—and often do—bury railways, roads, oases, wells and canals."

"But can't they be controlled at all?" I asked.

"Oh yes, it's one of our tasks here to learn how to do just that. The most successful way, it seems, is to plant special shrubs that bind the soil, like three-awn grass. The shrub *dzhuzgun* is also good. We've three varieties here. Local people call them 'sand binders' because their roots grip the sand and hold it. We grow them in our nurseries."

As we were both tired, I spread out my raincoat on the sand and we sat down. I offered Ostap a cigarette. He said he didn't smoke, but he examined my packet of Gauloises with interest. "Give my father one of these," he said. "The old fool smokes like a chimney."

On the ground we could take a close look around us. Hundreds of small ants and various kinds of beetles were scurrying about, leaving tiny tracks on the fine sand. Life was going on—and death. Several little grey lizards were busy hunting, dashing to and fro picking up ants with their long tongues and beetles with their jaws. But the insects seemingly paid not the slightest attention to this slaughter of their kith and kin, carrying on their business as if no predators were after them.

"There are over 400 kinds of beetles in Repetek," Ostap informed me, "but the insect world here has still not been well studied." He reached over and held up a small lizard that twisted about between his fingers.

"My snakes love them," he said. "We call them toadheads. There are three local kinds here." He released the lizard and it dived into the sand, disappearing in a split second.

"And what is that one?" I asked, pointing to a much larger lizard sitting, rather like a dog on its haunches, curling and uncurling its tail.

"Also a toadhead. This time a long-eared toadhead. Only those are not ears, but folds of skin at the end of the mouth. It is a jumpy little creature. Watch this." He stuck his twig in front of the lizard. It instantly dropped on all four legs, spreading them wide. Its whole body became taut, and

*Vigorously protecting its territory from intrusion, a hissing monitor lizard or varan whips out its tongue in a frightening display.*

as it gaped threateningly, the folds around its mouth turned blood red. It was quite a display. But instead of running away, it took a short jump towards the stick; then seeing no hostile reaction it scurried off.

"That one can bite, too," Ostap said. "And it can scare the daylights out of much bigger things—particularly birds. But the most interesting lizard here is our fringe-toed gecko. It's not grey like the other geckos; this one is a beauty. Blue, red and yellow, with a network of lines on its back as fine as lace. When it walks it raises its whole body and curls up its tail."

"Do you think we shall see one?" I asked.

"No, and I don't have one in my zoo either. Could never catch one. There is also the creature called *Scincum rubri*; if one so much as touches it, it throws off not only its tail, but part of the skin as well. Very sensitive. It comes out only at night; during the daytime it sleeps deep in the sand. The only way to see the desert wildlife properly is to come here at night with a powerful torch. Then one would see snakes, scorpions, tarantulas, phalanges. Everything, in fact. Want to come tonight?"

I said I could not, since I was taking a three o'clock—or was it one o'clock?—train back to Ashkhabad.

"Too bad," Ostap said. "Anyway you will eat with us. The old man's a good cook."

"I don't want to impose," I said.

"No trouble. The old man loves to talk to strangers. My mother died four years ago, and my younger brother is in the army in Odessa. Serving the motherland. I shall get us a bottle of good cognac at the village store."

I said that would be fine.

"But now we'd better get along, seeing how little time you have. You must see our white saxaul groves. They are like nothing on earth."

The white saxaul grove he took me to was indeed remarkable—even beautiful. It consisted of several gently rolling hills with scores of grotesquely twisted leafless trees, standing some distance from one another. The trees had nothing more than short bud-like knobs on their long branches. This produced hardly any shade, and silhouetted against the cloudless sky they looked fragile and delicate, rather similar to the trees in traditional Chinese paintings. A few prickly bushes, some blossoming, grew between them. About them common lemon-yellow butterflies were dancing. Ostap, however, was hell-bent on producing some samples of desert wildlife for me, including goitered gazelles, known locally as *djeirans*, and was urging me on. He was a tireless walker.

"There must be some *djeirans* here," he kept muttering. "Also foxes and hares. Some big snakes come out in the daytime, too, during this time of the year. Damn them, they are never there when you want them."

Luck was definitely against us. There were no gazelles and no snakes, only plains covered with camel prickle and astragal.

I was getting very tired and very thirsty. Suddenly, though, I thought I had struck oil.

"Look, there's your gecko!"

A fine-looking, large lizard, with a marvellously-etched design on its back, was sitting on a rock.

"That's no gecko! That's a net-back lizard. It loves the sand and can live in a moving dune. But that's no gecko." I could feel that Ostap was becoming rather depressed by my lack of zoological knowledge, as well as unhappy at not being able to find any bigger wildlife.

"It's funny. When you don't need them, they're crawling all over the place. Only yesterday I came across a terrific blunt-nosed viper. And I saw two *djeirans* right over there. But today they are hiding."

"Maybe we'd better start getting back," I suggested.

"But you haven't seen anything yet," Ostap protested.

"I've seen enough. I know what the desert is like. Let's start back."

So we turned back for the long tramp home. On the way we did catch a glimpse of an arrow snake, incredibly long and slender, but it darted away so fast I couldn't see it properly. By now it was so hot that even the lizards and tortoises were becoming scarce. Finally we came within sight of the village. Until then I thought that the most inspiring sight I had ever seen was the Pyramid of Cheops in the moonlight. I was wrong. It was the sight of the well as we entered the village. I'm not sure what the three village women thought of me as I begged them for water from their iron pail, but they gave me some which I gulped down, splashing it all over myself. Even though it tasted slightly salty, it was heavenly.

In five minutes I felt like a new man. Ostap, grinning, was watching me. Repetek, he told me, was "real fun" in July and August. It shared with Termez in Uzbekistan the distinction of being the hottest place in Central Asia. In both these places a temperature of 125° F. has been recorded. Only now I noticed that I had lost my raincoat somewhere. Still, at that moment, it seemed a cheap price to pay for getting out of the desert without serious mishap.

In a few minutes we reached the little house, not far from the railway station, that Ostap shared with his father. It was a typical Ukrainian *khatah*, neatly white-washed. Behind it there was a fairly large plot of land with tall trees providing ample shade. It was here that Ostap had his animal collection: two rows of wooden boxes filled with sand. Each box had a wooden tablet attached to it inscribed with the scientific name of its inmate.

Ostap's father was still wearing his pyjamas, but this time he had a row of six medals pinned to them. He also had on a pair of grey canvas shoes. The old man was sitting at a small wooden table under a large tree, smoking a cigarette and drinking beer. Next to the table stood a brass cauldron with glowing coals under it. Though the cauldron was covered, the aroma that escaped was tempting.

"Like the sand?" he asked with a grin that displayed his black teeth.

"He must come at night next time," Ostap said.

"It's an abomination, day or night," the old man said. "And one day I'm going to throw out all that filth, too," he added, indicating the boxes. "For this he had to go to school?"

The father and son went into a whispered conference, whereupon the old man departed while Ostap took me around to see his treasures. His snake collection was complete. A large blunt-nosed viper, about five feet long, was blissfully asleep in the corner of its box. There was a carpet viper, an arrow snake, and our old friend, the sand boa. Ostap was a truly dedicated zoologist, and he spoke about his inmates with warmth; he knew all their habits and idiosyncracies.

"Isn't that one a beauty!" he would say about one snake. "Look at the design on his back." And of another: "Note the way it curls its tail."

All three representatives of toadheads were here, as well as two species of gecko, some small lizards, including the fringe-toed lizard similar to the one we had met in the desert, and the lizard *Agama lehmanni*. Often mistakenly called a chameleon, this small lizard could change its colour from yellow to dark blue. The star of Ostap's lizard collection was a *varan* that he had named Misha. A large creature, it lay fast asleep half covered with sand. Apparently the *varan*, when frightened or pursuing a quarry, could move extremely quickly: 10 m.p.h., which is very fast for a lizard. Of the arachnids there were several huge black tarantula-like spiders of the order Solifugae, two or three scorpions, and a deadly *karakurt* spider—small, brown, with a red spot on its belly—which sat innocently in a glass jar.

When I asked Ostap how he coped with feeding the animals, he said it was not really a problem. He had to go out at night collecting beetles and small rodents for his *varan* and his snakes. In order to catch the

*Like most of the 45 species of snake in Russian Turkestan, the three snakes shown here are desert and semi-desert dwellers. To avoid the desert's extreme heat they seek the shade of plants and rocks or remain below ground until well after sunset, when they emerge to hunt their nocturnal prey—usually rodents and lizards. The daudius viper and the carpet viper are both poisonous, but the non-venomous green whip snake relies on the speed of its long thin body —it grows up to eight feet long—to catch and suffocate its prey.*

DAUDIUS VIPER

GREEN WHIP SNAKE

CARPET VIPER

nocturnal flying insects, he had rigged up an ingenious contraption: an old electric fan with a light bulb behind it, and a curved stove-pipe behind the bulb which led to a pail of water. Insects, attracted by the light, were blown into the pipe and wound up swimming in the pail. In one hour Ostap could collect enough food for all his animals.

Listening to Ostap talk was a pleasure as well as an education, and I regretted that we hadn't started here with his collections, instead of wandering all over the desert like two disorientated tortoises. When I said this to Ostap, he protested:

"Oh no, there's nothing like our desert. It's a place that gets into the blood. Look at my father. He cursed the desert for 50 years. Two years ago when he retired on his pension he went back to the Ukraine; but in two months he was back. He couldn't live without the sand. He still talks of going back, but he never will. The desert is hot, hard and difficult, but it's beautiful—once you know it."

At this point Ostap's father called us. Lunch—or dinner, as they call it here—was ready. We had some delicious *plov*, or pilaf—yellow rice with carrots—and pieces of fat mutton, all washed down with Turkestan's "cognac", a potent drink by any standard. Besides the food we also had a full quota of hair-raising war stories. Ostap's father, it seemed, had been largely responsible for the liberation of Europe from the "damned Fascists". During the meal two children, who were helping Ostap to maintain his little zoo, brought in a glass jar filled with beetles. Ostap gave them each a few copper coins.

"What are you going to do with all those creatures when you go back to Tashkent?" I asked.

"I'll take them into the desert and turn them loose. They belong here. I'm only keeping them while I'm writing my dissertation. Here in Repetek I can find everything for my subject: Turkestan desert fauna. That means 29 species of large and small mammals and rodents, 13 species of lizards, nine snakes, six arachnids, one tortoise and God only knows how many species of insects—thousands."

The old man spat on the ground. "What a country! In the Ukraine there are no snakes, and the most beautiful women in the world. And this young idiot is going to marry a *Turkmenka*. Imagine that!"

"An *Uzbechka*," Ostap corrected him.

"Well, horse-radish is no sweeter than wormwood," the old man said.

Then, while the old man was telling me about his future plans—a little house with a cherry orchard near Kharkov where there was no sand and no snakes—Ostap went inside. When he came out he had a sheet of paper with the scientific names of all the local animals written out in pencil. The most lurid sounding was *Phrynocephalus interscapularis*, which turned out to be a sand toadhead.

"You should go to Badkhyz," Ostap told me. "They have the richest nature complex in Turkmenistan there. Herds of *djeirans*, wild asses and goats. Also a lot of cobras."

"That's all he needs," the old man said. "God, what a country: worse than a mother-in-law."

I got up to make my way back to the station. Both men came to see me off. The train pulled in and I prepared to climb into a "hard wagon", as second-class railway coaches are known in the Soviet Union. I gave Ostap's father a pack of my precious French cigarettes and a cheap throw-away lighter as a souvenir. I was rewarded with a hug, a moist kiss on both cheeks, and a final piece of wry advice:

"Take my advice, comrade. If you see a desert, run and don't ever look back."

As the train pulled away across the undulating sand dunes under the pinkish desert haze, I heard a gruff ornithological admonition:

"Don't leave without paying!"

NATURE WALK **/ The Realm of the Wild Ass**

When I arrived in Badkhyz, the 185,000 acre reserve at the southernmost tip of Turkmenistan where the Soviet Union borders Afghanistan, I found it hard to believe that I was on the edge of one of the world's largest deserts. It was a gentle April day, and the rolling hills, or *bairs* as they are called, were thickly cloaked in rich green grass and dotted with multi-coloured islands of wild flowers. And all around me was the pink-and-white froth of trees in blossom —almond, cherry, apricot, plum.

The profusion was astonishing since Badkhyz, like the rest of Turkestan, suffers from a dearth of fresh water. The annual rainfall is only nine inches. Fortunately it is concentrated by impervious strata into springs that begin to flow in February and last through until May. Plants and animals have adapted themselves to make the most of this extended wet season and to endure the drawn-out, hot, dry summers and the short, sharp winters.

As I prepared to set out, in hopes of seeing the rare animals that thrive in this area, the almost ceaseless wind that gives the place its poetic name (*badkhyz* means "the wind has risen") rustled through the grasses, transforming the hills into an undulating sea of dark green.

I was on the lookout in particular for lizards and snakes, both of which come in dozens of varieties here, and for the hooved animals that have made Badkhyz famous—graceful gazelles, massive goats, and wild asses or *kulan* as they are known locally. These last had been all but wiped out before the reserve was established: it was chiefly to preserve them that Badkhyz was set up.

**Towards the Great Gorge**

My guide was a Turkmen biologist who lives in a village about 20 miles south of Badkhyz, almost on the Afghan border. Because he loved to speak English, he had given himself what he considered to be a high-sounding name—Robert. We were to make a tour of the elliptically-shaped reserve, working our way south-west across broad savannahs thick with pistachio trees, Badkhyz's most precious botanical treasure. We would then travel through terrain that varies from mountains and ravines to patches of desert towards our final destination, the Er-Oylan-Duz depression. This is a magnificent gorge whose stark cliffs and gleaming salt lake lie just outside the reserve's southern boundary.

Only a few rough trails wind

ER-OYLAN-DUZ DEPRESSION

through Badkhyz, so our journey, in Robert's ancient Soviet version of a jeep or Land Rover, was on the bumpy side. So was our conversation. Robert was a mine of information, but his English tended to be eccentric. When I commented on the greenness, he replied, "You please

LARK ON FERULA TUFT

linger two-three months and you perceive big change. Aridity and torridity are climactic here."

Torridity was certainly not much in evidence at the moment. This spring was even wetter than usual and the place was at its best. "Please perceive ferulas," Robert said suddenly, pointing to a cluster of bizarre-looking plants some six or seven feet tall. "They make your oculars gay, no?" The giant ferulas were indeed striking—thick spears topped by umbrella-like spreads of tufty green. They covered many hills in dense thickets, their feathery branches providing nesting space for larks and other small birds.

Ferulas have a singular life-cycle. Every spring the stem of each plant shoots up to its full height, then withers away in summer. Though apparently dead, it survives for six to nine years, but only once in its lifetime does it burst into bloom, blazing with spectacular greenish-yellow flowers. As the lofty stem waves in the breeze, the seeds, which are winged, are scattered up to 15 yards away. Only then, having completed its life cycle, does the plant die. The next spring new ferulas appear, reaching their full height within about six weeks.

### A Herd of Wild Asses

Suddenly Robert braked the jeep and gestured towards a distant ferula-covered slope. "*Kulan!*" he exclaimed breathlessly. It was incredibly good luck to come upon them so soon. I strained my eyes.

They were hard to make out, because their tawny-gold summer coats almost disappeared against the tall grass. There were about 30, grazing in a long file. If anything had startled them, they would have wheeled and run abreast in a single straight line, their usual defensive formation. We got out of the jeep silently and tiptoed towards them. I was eager for a closer look; like most people, I had seen wild asses only in zoos. When the preservation programme began, there were probably no more than 152 *kulan* throughout Turkestan. Today there are about 1,200 in Badkhyz alone, and probably another 500 or so across the border in Afghanistan.

As we edged towards the herd, Robert imparted in whispers some

*A FERULA SHOOT*

of his store of information concerning *kulan*. Water is their chief preoccupation, for they cannot last more than two or three days without drinking. They have no problem in the spring, when the hills are covered with rich, juicy fodder. But during the intense summer heat they must go either to one of the two permanent springs within the reserve or to the protected "canteens" on the Tedzhen and Murghab rivers to east and west, a few miles beyond the Badkhyz borders. They approach water cautiously, explained Robert, usually in the cool of the evening, each herd preceded by a leader which makes sure that there are no other animals about. Once given the all-clear, the *kulan* throw caution to the winds, gambolling, splashing and emitting noisy, donkey-like

*A GROVE OF FERULAS*

GRAZING KULAN

race horse—and *that* seems a point in favour of those who insist that this lean, swift, handsome creature should be termed a horse.

The *kulan* are clearly thriving, but their numbers have reached their upper limit, for the Badkhyz water supply is not large enough to support the growing population. Even now, during arid spells, Badkhyz and Afghan *kulan* wander back and forth to each others' territory in search of water.

There are few other places in Central Asia that can provide the space and water the animals need. (One of them is the Barsa-Kel'mes Island in the Aral Sea, where seven *kulan* mares and one stallion were sent in 1953. Unfortunately, the

brays. Some claim that the *kulan* should be termed a horse, not an ass, but its bray is a strong justification for the more usual classification.

We were now quite close to the grazing animals, and I was struck firstly by their diminutive stature— they are little more than four feet high at the shoulder—and then by their grace and beauty. The *kulan* is lithe, long-legged and smooth-muscled, with a dark furry stripe, like an extension of its mane, down the centre of its back, and a jaunty tail that ends in a trim little brush. "Such beautitude," Robert murmured. Suddenly they all bolted and disappeared. They were nervous, said Robert, because the mating season was barely over. Their speed amazed me; a *kulan* can run at more than 40 miles an hour, as fast as any

A FORAGING KULAN

*A FIELD OF POPPIES*

stallion proved impotent, and a replacement had to be sent in 1955. By 1963, 41 *kulan* were living and breeding there.) *Kulan* from Badkhyz have been supplied to many zoos, where they are now thriving in captivity, but it is unlikely that herds will be introduced into the natural environment elsewhere.

We got back into the jeep, but the going was slow, because we kept stopping to stroll among wild flowers. As I sauntered ankle-deep in a field of red poppies, Robert cautioned; "Please be most careful not to set foot upon slithering snakes." The undergrowth was full of them,

although, he added reassuringly, no snake—even the local species of cobra—will ever attack a man unless provoked.

Before long, we encountered our first cobra. The native variety is much smaller than its Indian cousin; but it is hooded just as evilly, and it is equally venomous. Ours was nestling snugly under some tulips, and it ignored us as we examined these wild descendants of the blooms that were transplanted to Holland four centuries before. The tulip is native to Turkestan and Asia Minor and gets its name from the Turkish *tulbant* and the Persian *dulbant*,

*COBRA AMONGST THE POPPIES*

*A DESERT TORTOISE*

both words for "turban". It did not reach western Europe until a Flemish diplomat took some bulbs back home in the 16th Century.

A little further along, we spotted a desert tortoise, one of the many reptiles that provide food for the area's predatory birds and animals. Like everything else in this semi-desert, they are most active in the spring, and we could hear them shuffling through the grass whenever we stopped. Then we had another stroke of luck. As we watched, a tiny snake not much larger than an earthworm worked its way up to the surface from beneath some yellow tulips. This creature's Russian name is *slepozmeijka,* which means, literally, "small blind snake". It lives underground where it feeds on ants and slugs and ventures out into the open air only in the wet season.

### The Elusive Cheetah

As we drove on, we saw several more herds of *kulan* grazing in the distance, and Robert spoke with a proprietary air of the other animals we might meet. There are 48 mammal species in Badkhyz. He began to reel them off—the boar, the hyena, the wolf, the honey badger, the unique lynx-like caracal, the fox and the gazelle or *djeiran*, which, he boasted, was "the best living ornament of our nature".

"What about the *gepard*?" I interrupted, using the native name for the rare Asiatic cheetah. It is a beautiful thing—sinuous and sleek with a gleaming saffron coat dappled by dark spots. I had seen two in the Moscow zoo, but they have almost disappeared in the wild. Russian zoology books list Badkhyz as their only remaining U.S.S.R. habitat. Robert made a wry face. He didn't like to admit that anything might possibly have become extinct in this

*WILD TULIPS*

protected wilderness. He raised his eyes to the cloudless sky: "Mystification!" he sighed. At best there were never many in Badkhyz and none has been seen for about two decades. No one knows what went wrong. "Biological incomprehension!" commented Robert.

*Gepard* are formidable runners—like their African counterparts, they can repeatedly top 60 m.p.h.—and can catch any prey they choose; so they could not have died of starvation. Every once in a while, even now, a *djeiran* carcass is found that looks as though it had been killed by a *gepard's* long, sharp, unretract-

*A BLIND SNAKE*

able claws. Surely this was proof, said Robert—more, it seemed, in an attempt to convince himself than me—that a few still lurked in the inaccessible rocky hills.

Soon we came upon a herd of *djeiran*, and my disappointment over the absent *gepard* vanished. It would have been sad to think of them somewhere over the horizon menacing these delicate little gazelles (the largest weigh only about 60 pounds). *Djeiran* have had trouble enough. They were almost wiped out by hunters before the law stepped in some 20 years ago. And poachers still, to use Robert's word, "mortify" far too many; their flesh is delicious and their pelts valuable, making the

*A GREEN BEETLE*

finest suede. Badkhyz's *djeiran* population is now over 5,000; and while they still have their natural enemies —wolves, leopards, foxes, hyenas, birds of prey—at least one of the two offspring that each female bears annually usually manages to survive. The *djeiran* did not seem to mind our approaching quite close.

They raised their heads, looked at us calmly and went back to their grass.

The field where they grazed was thick with wild flowers. Some had exquisite little bell-shaped blossoms that fluttered in the breeze on long slender stems like sea anemones wafted by a gentle current. Others, a variety of lily that grows nowhere except in Central Asia, reminded me of larkspur, with flowerlets packed tightly together on tall stalks. And I saw tulips in the most improbable places. Some had forced their way up through rocks, and seemed to survive on sheer courage.

### The Insect Swarms

Multi-coloured insects buzzed about the flowers. A pair of burnet

*A LOCAL VARIANT OF THE POPPY—BONGARDIA CHRYSOGONUM*

moths, wings streaked with brilliant scarlet, mated as they clung precariously to the lower leaves of a plant. As I bent down to peer at a vivid green beetle, Robert announced that Badkhyz, superior in so many things, can also claim the national record for the number and variety of insects. About 200 previously unknown kinds of bug are classified every year, he said. Sometimes insects come in overwhelming swarms, and then they are dealt with summarily by birds. In recent years there have been two locust plagues, and both times great flocks of pink starlings, strangers to Badkhyz, arrived days in advance, as if forewarned, to devour the pests.

*TULIP IN ROCK-STREWN GROUND*

*MATING BURNET MOTHS*

We had just returned to our jeep, when I saw, outlined on a nearby slope, an ugly grey reptile about four feet long. With its body held high on scaly legs, it looked like a miniature dinosaur. It was a *varan*, a wolf among lizards, one of Badkhyz's most vicious denizens. It is, in my opinion, a most unattractive creature. It roams desert and steppe, gobbling up smaller lizards, tortoises, rodents and birds, and it will even, on occasion, eat its own young. We stopped the car and walked cautiously towards it. It hissed, bared its sharp teeth and lashed its powerful tail. "Stand clear!" Robert shouted. A wallop from the tail would have meant a painful bruise, and its bite inflicts a deep, unpleasant wound. To my relief, it turned and made off.

We were by now at the edge of the pistachio savannah, and as we drove along Robert said that the *varan* had undoubtedly been preying upon the small animals that live among these nut trees, of which there are about 79,000 acres at Badkhyz. They stretched over hill after swelling hill, some in well separated stands and others in tight clumps. Most pistachio are from 15 to 20 feet tall.

*A TURKESTAN LILY*

*PISTACHIO BRANCH*

They live for nearly 400 years and there are a few that are believed to have survived for more than 1,000 years. In this part of Badkhyz there were countless saplings, a result of diligent annual sowing.

The pistachio is better adapted than any other nut tree to cope with a hot, arid climate. It can withstand the burning sun and seek out, through lateral roots that reach as far as 35 yards, whatever meagre moisture the earth has to offer. It grows best on high, hilly terrain; so Badkhyz, which rises to over 3,500 feet, offers ideal conditions. The Soviets permit a limited amount of commercial harvesting (too much, some of their own experts say) and the savannah teems with wild life in the autumn when the nutritious golden-green kernels—70 per cent fat, 23 per cent albumen—are ready to eat. Not only the *varan*, but many

*PISTACHIO GROVE*

other beasts—*kulan*, *djeiran*, goats, rodents, birds—come to feast upon the nuts—and each other. Many find the groves hospitable throughout the year. We soon met one of their most appealing inhabitants, a kitten-sized hedgehog with outsized ears, big round eyes and soft, strokable, greyish brown fur (but no prickles!). This variety exists only in Turkestan. Its scientific name, *Erinaceus auritus*, celebrates its ears, which, being so large, radiate a great deal of heat and thus keep the rest of the animal cool. These little hedgehogs are often kept as pets.

We drove out of the pistachio groves into wilder, treeless country.

A TURKESTAN HEDGEHOG

THE MAJESTIC HORNED SHEEP

It was becoming hot, and the hills were suddenly empty of animal life. Save for several sand hares that hopped off through the grass, only the reptile world seemed still alive. A brilliant red-striped coluber snake slithered across the trail; tortoises munched in the undergrowth and lizards sunned themselves contentedly on the rocks.

As we neared the Er-Oylan-Duz depression, Badkhyz's "Grand Canyon", the landscape grew more and more rugged, with rough escarpments towering above desert patches. I knew that the gorge stretched 17 miles and was 1,500 feet deep, but I was unprepared for the stark panorama that suddenly unfolded: jet black mountains falling sharply to a gleaming white salt lake, which was surrounded by masses of grotesque jutting rock formations. A number of rain-water pools glistened in the depths of the canyon. By mid-summer they and the lake would all have evaporated, and the vegetation that clung to the cliffs would mostly have been burned away.

The descent down the ravine was meant for mountain goats and not for men. Still, I was determined to try. Robert left me to it, promising to come back in a couple of hours. It was eerie, picking my way down, tensing involuntarily as dislodged stones bounced on the hard ground far below. The chasm stretched beyond my sight to either side. But in the clear air, the facing wall, some seven miles away, seemed almost within a stone's throw.

The gorge has its own distinctive wildlife, which was much in evidence. There were lizards everywhere, mostly *khorozan* agamas, which live only in Badkhyz. About six inches long, olive-skinned with

*DJEIRAN GAZELLES ON A RIDGE*

black and orange-yellow spots, they darted away at my approach in a flash of colour that blended quickly with the stony background.

**Sunset in the Dying Wind**

I surprised a herd of arkhar sheep drinking at a rain-water pool. Although elsewhere they have been almost hunted out of existence, here, like the *kulan* and the *djeiran*, they are valued and protected. A huge old male which must have weighed 250 pounds stared at me coldly from beneath his majestic curling horns. He recognized that I was no threat, and relaxed, thereby passing the word to the others that they could go on drinking in peace. When I climbed up again, panting but exhilarated, Robert, as good as his word, was waiting.

The light was beginning to fade. Thin dust whipped up by sudden gusts painted the sunset sky in startling colours—rose, amber, lavender, purple. Several *djeiran* stood on top of a rocky ridge silhouetted against this vivid backdrop.

Driving back through the lengthening shadows, we listened as the hills assumed with dusk a totally changed personality. The wind had died down to little more than a sigh. In the stillness we could hear the cries of small birds all around us—larks, orioles, jays, sparrows—welcoming the sunset coolness.

As darkness fell, the wilderness became alive in an altogether more ominous way. The mournful howling of jackals and the idiot laughter of hyenas were orchestrated with the piercing screeches of predatory night birds. Now and then came the desperate dying cries of their victims, as if to remind us that there is savagery as well as grandeur on the Badkhyz reserve.

ROCK FORMATIONS IN THE ER-OYLAN-DUZ

# 4/ The Colour of Paradise

*It is not earth that bears fruit, but water.*

TURKMEN PROVERB

It was a Sunday morning in Ashkhabad, very early, about six o'clock. I had had trouble sleeping and decided to go for a walk. The sun was already warm, but the city was still asleep and Lenin Prospect, the acacia-lined main street of Ashkhabad where trucks usually rumble all day long, was now deserted. About a quarter of a mile from my hotel, I saw a strange scene. A very old man with a wrinkled face and a white beard stood before one of the acacia trees, holding a little girl by the hand. He wore the typical dress of the *kumli*, or sand people: a long, striped cotton *khalat*, the kaftan still worn by old Turkmens, and a black sheep-fur hat. He spoke to the child in his native tongue, which I could not understand, nodding in the direction of the tree. The girl seemed confused and her large black eyes darted in my direction. Finally the old man gave the child a push. Closing her eyes, she quickly kissed the gnarled trunk, then dashed back to the old man and buried her pretty little face in his dusty kaftan. The old man smiled, stroking the girl's glossy black hair. He took her hand and they walked away.

I was bewildered and touched by this little scene. Was it some local superstition or ritual, perhaps part of Islamic tradition? There was no one around I could ask. But later I met a Russian girl, a journalist who loved and knew Turkestan well, and I asked her about the incident.

She was not sure what it meant. Perhaps the girl's grandfather wanted to teach her to respect all growing things. "To desert people," she explained, "every blade of grass is a dream, and every tree a miracle. Trees mean water and water means life. I've seen them bring their children for hundreds of miles to look at rivers and riverside forests. They stand on a riverbank as if hypnotized, looking at the flowing water. Afterwards they return to the desert. In small desert settlements I have seen people share their last bucket of water with their plants."

I asked if the scene I had witnessed might have anything to do with Islam. "Probably," she replied, "though few people go to mosques nowadays. But Islam is a religion born in the desert and by tradition Muslims venerate water and every living green thing. Green is the most popular colour in deserts and when the Arabs came here conquering the country for their Prophet, they fought under green banners. To them, it was the colour of Paradise, where all faithful Muslims killed in battle would go. In fact, the old Persian word *pairidaeza* simply means garden. Our people in Turkestan were quick to adopt this symbolism because the connection between all growing green things and life is so absolute here. You will understand all this when you see our rivers and our forests. The rivers give us life, but it is only because of our forests that we have any rivers at all."

I told her of my plan to trace the source of life from the deserts, along the rivers and then up to the mountains where the rivers are born. She agreed with my idea and added: "First and foremost, you must get to know the Amu Darya."

"Why the Amu Darya especially?" I asked. "What about the Syr Darya?"

"To the desert people, it is the Amu that matters," she replied. "It is by far the larger of the two, and they see it as the life-line Allah threw them when they were dying of thirst in the desert. They call it the mother river, and say that it has two daughters, the Karakum and the Kyzylkum. The 20,000 wells in the desert are all fed by the waters of the Amu Darya. Do you know what they say here? 'If the Amu dies today, we all die tomorrow'."

Fortunately the Amu Darya, though once much mightier, shows no signs of dying; it is still a powerful body of water. It rises as the Piandzh 16,000 feet up in the northern slopes of the Hindu Kush mountains and wends its way westward, forming much of the frontier between the U.S.S.R. and Afghanistan. Absorbing on its way thousands of small streams and several large tributaries, the Piandzh is joined by the Vakhsh river to become the Amu Darya, and veers north-west across the deserts to pour into the Aral Sea, some 1,500 miles from its source.

*Brown with sediment, a main channel of the Amu Darya meanders sluggishly across the river's flat delta area into the Aral Sea (foreground).*

*In the middle reaches of the delta, the Amu flows around islands of grass and shrubs.*

Unlike most rivers, it has two flood periods instead of one. The spring flood, lasting from April to May, is formed by the thawing snow. A second flood period begins in June, when hot weather causes the rapid melting of mountain glaciers. Sometimes the two periods follow one another so closely they combine into one and the Amu's high-water period lasts for five months at a stretch. In flood the Amu reaches widths of a mile in places and its chocolate-coloured water, which carries twice as much alluvium as the Nile, deposits its fertile sediment along the length of its flooded banks.

Though impressive now, the Amu Darya is only a shadow of its former self. It was famous in ancient history under the name of Arax, or Oxus— as a river of gargantuan proportions. In the 5th Century B.C., Herodotus wrote: "The river itself has forty branches all of which, with the exception of one, which flows into the Caspian Sea, lose themselves in the sand." Although Herodotus may have been guilty of rounding off his numbers, his geography seems to have been generally correct. It is well known that the Amu Darya did once flow into the Caspian instead of the Aral Sea, by the dry bed known today as the West Uzboy.

Two centuries later, the armies of Alexander the Great had to spend five days and nights crossing the river, which they did by floating across on animal skins sewn together and inflated. And at the beginning of the Christian era the Greek historian and geographer Strabo described the Arax as the mightiest stream in Central Asia, indicating that its main channel now emptied into the Aral Sea.

Today the Amu Darya owes its impoverishment both to accident and to man. When the river swung north to the Aral Sea, it parted company with several large tributaries that had once fed it on its way through the desert. The Amu now no longer receives water after it bursts out of the mountains. Instead, it loses vast amounts by evaporation and seepage. But there are other more important causes of the river's depletion: irrigation and the destruction of the forests that grow along its banks.

These riverside forests, known as *tugai*, are unlike anything else found in Turkestan. Composed of dense reeds, trees and shrubs, they vary from half a mile to two miles in width and are sometimes so impenetrable they have been nicknamed *dzhungli* (jungle). The *tugai* keep the river on its course and prevent it from spilling into the desert by binding the sand and soil along the banks. Although the *tugai* themselves are often flooded, they are usually rooted firmly enough to direct the river back to its original bed when the water subsides. Even if the water does wash them away, they grow back so fast that they can normally replace themselves within a year or two.

The *tugai*, the Amu Darya and the relationship of one to the other were explained to me with rich eloquence on a flight to Chardzhou by my neighbour, Nikifor Petrovich. He was a massive grey-haired man, wearing a small embroidered skull cap. But his first words to me betrayed his real origin.

"The Amu, ulcers to her soul, is a wonderful river," he said.

A Siberian! Only a Siberian would utter this particular oath, which can be used both in anger and in affection. It so startled the playwright Chekhov when he heard it that he concluded "a Siberian would wish ulcers to everyone and everyone's soul 20 times a day".

"She's full of tricks, she is," continued Nikifor Petrovich with a tender note in his gruff voice. "One has to eat a ton of salt before one learns all of them." He could speak with authority. Although he had been born in Siberia, he had come to Turkestan as a young boy with his father, a railway worker. He had become a river skipper and for 40 years had sailed the Amu Darya between Chardzhou and Nukus on the river's delta. He was now returning after a holiday in Siberia.

He loved the great stream, but was quite pessimistic—often for dramatic effect, as I later learned—about its future. "She's not the river she was when I first saw her," he complained. "Man, ulcers to his soul, has raped her. She's a cripple now, with much of the blood drained out of her. She gets feebler with each passing season as her water is diverted here and there for irrigation or a new canal. She's not a cow; you can't milk her like this. The Amu is feeding the whole desert, and that's more important. They will have their new cotton fields and orchards, but then the desert wells will start running dry. One can't sell the same goat at two bazaars. Even now, in summer, steamers get stuck in the shallows and flounder like pigs in a mud puddle. When I sailed her, one could sail with one's eyes shut."

Nikifor Petrovich did not love progress. He told me Turkestan was a much better place 40 years ago, "before all those engineers came in and started fooling around with dams and the *tugai*".

"What about the *tugai*?" I asked.

"The *tugai* are for the Amu like rails for a railway. Destroy the *tugai* and the Amu will start wandering all over the desert like a gypsy horse-thief. And they've cut them down. Those settlers from Russia went mad cutting the *tugai* down, killing everything that lived, and putting the land to the plough. But you know the Russian saying, 'We were laughing-selling-buying, counted cash and started crying'? The next spring, the river started washing away their fields and homes like a cow licking something off her nose. The Amu isn't the Volga; you can't fool around with her like that. She's like a Krasnoyarsk wife: you hit her with a samovar and she hits back with an axe." (Siberian women have a reputation for sturdiness.)

"The *tugai*," Nikifor Petrovich went on, "are worlds of their own, with their own flora and fauna and a climate that remains cool and fresh when the deserts around are burning. When I was young," he reminisced, "pheasants used to rise in clouds as the steamer went by, deer came to the banks to watch us, and boars used to swim along begging for swill. It was beautiful, and now all you see are crows."

But wasn't all unauthorized wood-cutting strictly forbidden by law? "Let me tell you something," he said. "All those laws are not worth a piece of dry camel dung on a stick. They write them in Ashkhabad and Tashkent and nobody reads them. It's too late anyway; they should have written them 50 years ago. The *tugai* used to be so thick even a tax collector could not get through, but now there are holes in them as wide as a Kazakh's trousers. Mark my words, sooner or later those engineers and agronomists coming here from Russia are going to murder the river with their canals and clearings. God, ulcers to his soul, knew what he did when he created this river, but he sure made a hell of a mistake when he created those learned idiots."

I was relieved to hear when I arrived in Chardzhou that, despite Nikifor Petrovich's pessimism, there are still long stretches where these forests hug the river. I was able to visit a few of them on a brief boat trip upstream from Chardzhou. I found them very impressive. The Amu Darya was in partial flood and without *tugai* it would have been impossible to tell where the banks were. Two ribbons of green formed by the tops of trees framed the swollen river. I could easily imagine the water going wild in the desert were it not for these barriers.

In places where the water was lower, blossoming bushes filled the air with a delicate fragrance. The yellow flowers of this tree are still used by river people to cure a variety of ills, including simple stomach aches. Poplars, willows and tamarisks covered with small white or violet flowers made up the rest of the forest vegetation. The trees and shrubs were festooned with the local climber, scientifically called *Clematis orientalis*, but which is known locally as *lomonos*, meaning "nose-breaker", a wry reference to the *tugai's* tangled impenetrability. These sturdy climbers bind the trees together and help them withstand the onslaught of mud-heavy floods.

I did not see any of the beautiful Amu Darya pheasants, although I was told they were still found in the densest *tugai*. Boars were numerous: they are excellent swimmers and show no fear of the floods, which drown rodents, foxes and hares. Boars have sometimes been known to swim across the whole width of the river.

Back at Chardzhou, I watched the churning waters rush by. I knew that when the melting of glaciers and snowfields ceased the water supply would taper off, the Amu fall and sandy islands and spits begin to appear. But the Amu never actually runs dry and there is navigation throughout the year. What ensures this flow? The answer lies in Turkestan's lush hillside forests, and it was to the forests that I next directed my attention. I went on to Tashkent to consult Professor F. N. Rusanov, founder of Tashkent's Botanical Gardens, one of the foremost institutions of this kind in the world. Rusanov was already quite old, but his agility and enthusiasm belied his age.

"Forests mean everything to us," he said. "They are life. Life! Without them this country would be a sea of mire for the two spring months, and an absolute desert for the rest of the year. By August, there would not be a single river flowing. Nowhere in the world are the forests as important as in Turkestan. Nowhere!"

Since the rainfall in Turkestan is minimal, he explained, the entire country, up to the Kazakhstan steppes in the north, depends for its water supply on the Pamir and Tien Shan mountains. There is enough accumulated ice and snow in the mountains to flood all Turkestan to a depth of two feet. The annual spring thaw of snow and the melting of glaciers in summer provide gigantic pulses of water, but much of this flow would be wasted without the forests. They act as sponges, absorbing the water in their live vegetation, dead plants, litter and soil, and slowly doling it out to the country through the long dry seasons.

The forests have a number of other crucial rôles besides regulating the flow of melted snow. During the rare but powerful downpours, they restrain surface run-off, thus preventing slopes from being eroded by sudden floods. They act as a barrier against avalanches of snow and mud, which can devastate entire regions. And they provide valuable cover that shields the snow from the direct heat of the sun and that prevents a large proportion of the meltwater from being rapidly evaporated by solar radiation.

Rusanov took me into an office and showed me a large hydro-

*These outcroppings of Kirgizian sandstone—known as The Oxen because of their humped-back form—combine the sand-baked colours of*

the desert, a green setting and an imposing rock face, thus dramatizing the west-east transition from desert to foothills to high mountains.

graphical map of Turkestan, a fantastic maze of blue lines of various thickness. "Think of the human body with its network of blood vessels," he said. "The smallest brook in Turkestan, every stream, every well, is part of a similar circulatory system. And it is up to our mountains continually to pump blood into this system. They are our hearts, and they beat annually at regular intervals. But not a drop of this precious water must be wasted or allowed to go astray, and our forests act as banks, storing Turkestan's life-blood and dispensing it gradually. Go and see these bloodbanks for yourself. In the Chatkal range you will find two fine reserves—the Chatkal and the Sarychelek. And then, for real beauty, try to see the walnut groves."

Rusanov left to visit his plantations, where, as a friend of his later told me, "he knew every plant by its first name", and the next day I set out for the hills. The nearer of the two places he had mentioned was the Chatkal Forest Management. It was a mere 40 miles from Tashkent, a short journey by car. From these hills, which are foothills of the Tien Shan and form an arc bending to the south-west, pour several tributaries of the Syr Darya. On my way I spotted the source of one of these rivers, the Chingan. It was at the foot of Mount Chingan and I stopped the car to watch 12 small springs fed by melt-water in the high mountains burst out of the rock and form a stream that would eventually pour into the Syr Darya.

Some ten miles farther on, at 7,000 feet, I crossed into the Chatkal Forest Management and continued on foot. It was not the well-groomed park its name suggested, but rather a large stretch of raw nature rescued from man. One hundred thousand acres of absolutely wild mountain woodland stretched away to a majestic backdrop of distant mountains, wearing glistening snow caps like the white sheepskin *telpeks* of the Turkmen herdsmen. The trees were in full leaf and the green meadows and glades were dotted with islands of spring flowers—red poppies, wild tulips, blue irises, daisies and forget-me-nots with gaily patterned butterflies among the flowers. The scenery reminded me of the Swiss Alps, but seemed more rugged, more virile.

After a few minutes' walk, I encountered a squat and rugged Uzbek of indeterminate age, with antediluvian deposits in the wrinkles of his face and under his cracked nails. He was kneeling in front of an ant-hill, scooping out the contents with his bare hands and putting them into a burlap bag. Ants crawled all over him, but he paid them no attention. He explained to me that he was collecting the ants for his father, who was suffering from arthritis and whose pains could be relieved only by

*Fed by numerous mountain streams, the Chatkal Forest Management is one of the few lush areas of Russian Turkestan. Its greenery is short-lived, however. By summer, when the rivers have shrunk, the flowers wilt and the grass yellows.*

ant bites and bee stings. But when he learned that I planned to explore the forest, he shook off his insects and took up a rifle that was leaning against a tree, eyeing me suspiciously.

"I'll come with you," he said. "Some parasites have no respect for the forest." I assured him I had no intention of chopping down trees or breaking shrubs, and he soon became more friendly.

He was delighted to learn I was an American citizen. "My name is Ibrahim," he said, "just like your President Lincoln." He proved himself a mine of information and as we walked in this sylvan wilderness, Ibrahim told me about the place.

The area's lush vegetation, he said, is protected by the configuration of the mountains, which shield the region from icy Siberian winds in winter, and from the hot arid air of Afghanistan in the summer. Although the climate is continental, with hot summers and cold winters, the temperatures are never as extreme as in the desert.

Ibrahim insisted there were some 1,500 varieties of trees and shrubs in the Chatkal forest and invited me to admire its beauty. "This is the most beautiful place in the world," he stated, "better even than Niagara Falls." This was apparently the American landmark he admired most. "Look at that mountain, will you? Isn't she a beauty. And look at that spring. Its water is so cold it numbs your mouth. And look at those birds; we have 200 species here and most of them sing." The forest was indeed alive with bird-song, making it much more cheerful than the Siberian forests I had known, where most of the birds are silent. But Ibrahim was particularly interested in the botanic splendours of his forest. He would bend down to some little plant and grow ecstatic. "Just look at that, it's a . . . "—and here he gave the local name—"the rarest plant in Uzbekistan. You'll never see anything like this anywhere, not even at Niagara Falls."

"Everything grows tremendously fast here," he went on. "It's the air and the soil and the sun. This place is Turkestan's sub-tropical region." Would it be as green in September as it is now? No, admitted Ibrahim, the present spring magnificence would not last long. In the summer the flowers would disappear and the grass would turn yellow, even though, as he put it, "the earth would never grow thirsty." But in the autumn, the Chatkal forest was even more beautiful. "The mountains are like fire, with all the leaves turning red and purple. You must come back then, this is a beautiful place. Much better than . . . "

"Yes, yes," I said, "but I've heard there are other places in the Chatkal mountains that can rival the Niagara Falls. What about the famous walnut forests?" In reply, Ibrahim showed me some walnut saplings and generously invited me to come back in 50 years.

"What about Sarychelek?"

"An uncultured place," he said; "what do you want to go there for? We have wildcats, porcupines, frogs, mountain goats. You just stay here. You'll be able to see them all."

But I had to leave him. To the sound of frogs croaking in a distant pool, I made my way to the car and left for Tashkent to plan my next trip.

I was sorriest to have missed those walnut forests, which are a unique feature of Turkestan. Composed almost entirely of walnuts, interspersed with occasional small maples, they have a peculiar charm. A 19th-Century Russian traveller to Turkestan, V. Vitkovitch, was overwhelmed by their beauty: "The mountains are covered with the lacey velvet of nut trees . . . In the forest itself, the ground is covered with a thick carpet of dead leaves emitting a fragrant freshness. . . . As one wanders through this enchanted place one becomes amazed at the power of life contained in these trees. The branches of some of them touch the soil and have sprouted roots of their own, like living green arcades. One cannot get enough of the beauty of the place, enough of its natural splendour, its marvellous air." As it happened I finally did see the thick and dark green canopy of these forests—from the air as I flew by helicopter north, over the Chatkal range towards the Sarychelek Forest Management. It was a brief taste of the beauty Vitkovitch had described.

Sarychelek is one of the remotest forest areas of Turkestan. The helicopter left me some two miles from the forest and I covered the rest of the distance on foot. It is an enchanting place with a tiny, picturesque mountain lake hemmed in by steep and densely wooded slopes. The lake's cold water is so clear that a stone can be seen disappearing 20 feet or so below the surface among the gnarled trunks of old trees that have been shaken into it by the area's frequent earthquakes. The surrounding area is a botanical museum that combines trees native to Turkestan and Afghanistan with northern species—fir and silver birch—and southern varieties of fruit trees.

Among the trees are some gorgeous stands of Turkestan mountain juniper. Some of the Sarychelek junipers are said to be 1,000 years old, and even these still produce berries rich in the oil and acids so widely used in folk medicine. But the principal value of the juniper is its function as a soil binder. A highly developed root system enables them to withstand strong winds and erosion. Indeed, their tenacity is fabulous: I have seen junipers hug wind-swept crags with most of their roots hanging in the air like the tentacles of some colossal sea monster. Especially crucial is their rôle in spring, when torrents of melt-water must be filtered down to the Naryn Valley and eventually to the Syr Darya. As I watched the streams trickling through their knotted roots, the junipers seemed a fitting symbol of the whole forest "sponge" that filters the floods pouring down from the high mountains.

# Mountainsides in Bloom

In vivid contrast to the barren and monochromatic deserts, the mountain landscapes of eastern Turkestan at times offer a kaleidoscope of colour. Because the slopes provide a wide variety of growing conditions, they support plants and trees with origins as diverse as the Mongolian steppes, the shores of the Mediterranean and the Himalayas. The many types of flora are segregated in clearly defined habitats that vary with altitude.

The low-lying slopes rising from the desert (around 1,500 feet) are the driest and hottest, but they support a surprisingly luxuriant growth when the ephemeral plants burst into bloom during the short spring rains. The perennials, hyacinths, irises and tulips, also blossom at the beginning of April, followed quickly by blue gentians. Towards midsummer, hardier flowers, notably blue larkspur and the unusual umbrella-shaped scaligeria, dot the slopes. By August, when soil temperature can reach 150°F, nearly all of these flowers wither and die.

Higher up the climate becomes milder. In the less arid foothills between 2,000 and 5,000 feet, waves of meadow grass sprinkled with yellow and violet irises provide a brilliant spring display. A thousand feet higher the mountainous steppe zone has grass cover through the summer, and the southerly areas provide such wild fruit trees as apricot, pomegranate and almond.

The richest vegetation is found in the cooler regions up to nearly 10,000 feet, where the soil is nourished by rain and the run-off from the snows above. There are rich leaf forests of walnut trees as well as plum and apple trees that flower in spring, and the maple *Acer turkestanicum* and barberry bushes that flower in summer and winter. Among the forests are meadows filled with geraniums, water lilies and thickets of wild rose and honeysuckle.

In the harsh sub-alpine and alpine zones just below the snow-line, vegetation becomes sparse again, and it is here that some of Turkestan's specialities are found: the cold-resistant *Onosma dichroanthum*, which ranges in colour from yellow to purple; the *Morina kokanica* with its poppy-shaped leaves and pink flowers; and the rare *Pulsatilla kostyczewii*, which blooms only a few times in its life, its fruits trailing magnificent whitish plumes that help the dispersal of seeds in the high mountain winds.

PULSATILLA KOSTYCZEWII

*MORINA KOKANICA*

BARBERRY BERRIES

*ONOSMA DICHROANTHUM*

ACER TURKESTANICUM

*WHITE KUBSHYNKA*

# 5/ The Roof of the World

*The mountains of Kirgizia and Tadzhikistan were already visible, royal with height and solemn with snow, flying the colours of the dawn like battle flags from their crests.*

LAURENS VAN DER POST/ *JOURNEY INTO RUSSIA*

"We are very rich," an Uzbek journalist told me as we sat in a roadside *chai-khana* a few miles outside Tashkent, devouring a delicious mutton *plov*, "and do you know what is the greatest treasure we have?"

"The ocean of oil under the Karakum," I guessed.

"Wrong," he said. "There it is!" He pointed south. Beyond a line of poplar trees and hazy purple hills rose a narrow band of snow, gleaming against the deep blue of the sky: the first ranks of the Pamir and Tien Shan mountains. I hesitated before replying, so he continued.

"When I was a small boy," he said, "my great-grandfather was still alive. He died when he was 110. And every day of his life he prayed five times in accordance with Muslim law. But instead of facing Mecca, he faced our mountains. The *mullah* of our mosque remonstrated with him, but the old man told him: 'I went to Mecca and I saw the evening star over the Ka'aba, the Prophet's black stone. It was a dead stone. But our mountains are alive.' The *mullah* called him a heathen, but my great-grandfather did not listen. Instead he told him to go and kiss a camel. Then he turned to me and said: 'Always pray to our mountains, my boy. Allah's most priceless treasure lies buried there, under the snow.'" My friend smiled wistfully. "He was a wise old devil, and he was right about the mountains, bless their cold hearts."

"You mean the water?" I asked.

"Of course. The frozen water of the glaciers."

I was due to leave for the mountains the following day. As I packed my bags that night, my friend's story came back to me. "The mountains are alive," his great-grandfather had said. It was odd to hear them described like that, since it was the direct opposite of another opinion I had heard only a few days before. A lorry driver who spent his life crossing and recrossing the high Pamirs told me with a good deal of feeling: "God must have made that mountain wasteland in a moment of utter despair. There is more life in the Karakum than there. At least the wind stirs the sands in the desert. In the mountains there is nothing but dead stone." Marco Polo had said much the same thing when he crossed the Pamirs in the 13th Century, "passing many rivers and desert tracts, without seeing any habitations or the appearance of verdure." Even today, 90 per cent of the region is uninhabitable.

On the other hand, I could think of several ways in which the mountains were alive. On a number of occasions I heard the local people speak of them as if they were living things. "They look at peace today.... They look angry tonight ... They are smiling this morning ... " These people know only too well that the source of life is locked up in the glaciers, thawing in spring to form torrents of melt-water that roar down through the deep valleys, ultimately feeding the two great rivers and the nomads' wells in the Karakum and Kyzylkum deserts. They also know that the mountain's topography is constantly changing, shaken by frequent earthquakes, transformed overnight by avalanches sweeping down the sheer slopes, cracked by the powerful expansion of freezing water. In addition, there are various forms of life that manage to survive in the isolated areas below the permanent snow-line: specially adapted plants, animals and small groups of mountain people eking a meagre existence from the hostile white giants.

My plan was to concentrate on the Pamirs, exploring on foot as much as possible, and then journey briefly into the Tien Shan, by which time I hoped to have formed my own opinion of the mountains. Before getting down to details, however, I wanted an overall impression of the great barrier that straddles the border between the Soviet Union and China, and that can only be had from the air. Luckily there is a flight from Tashkent to Khorog in the western Pamirs that passes over some of the most dramatic sections of the range, including Communism Peak, which, at over 24,500 feet, is its highest mountain. The next morning, with Lev Ustinov and Arkady Semonian, I took off on the first stage of our expedition. We flew due south, climbing steadily. When the morning mist cleared, we were already close to the mountains. Below us stretched the lush Alai Valley, the finest high pasture in Central Asia, and ahead rose a jagged wall of ice, shimmering against the sky. As we approached, the wall seemed to extend in all directions until it became a great icy dome. It looked like the roof of a gigantic cathedral, with 20,000-foot riders for flying buttresses—a vista that inspired the Russian explorers who opened up the area in the 19th Century to call the Pamirs *krysha mira*, the roof of the world.

We were still gaining height, and as our view widened the vista was transformed yet again, turning this time into an endless ocean of ice. We could see line after line of parallel ridges, the characteristic formation of the Pamirs, running east-west across our path. This knotted mass of rock and ice, wave after wave, spans over 35,000 square miles and is the largest mountain range in the world after the Himalayas, of which it is an extension. As we approached the mighty bulk of Communism Peak, I could see the icy tongue of a particularly large glacier scarring its northern slope. It was the Fedchenko Glacier, my neighbour told me proudly, the largest in the Soviet Union, named after one of the great explorers of the Pamirs, Alexei Fedchenko. It contains more water than the Aral Sea, yet it is only one of a thousand or more glaciers in the Pamirs.

These natural storage tanks are the result of centuries, even millenia, of snowfalls. In the region of "perpetual snows" above 13,000 feet, about 65 inches of snow fall annually. Since this exceeds the annual wastage by both melting and evaporation, the depth of the snow increases each year. Melting and refreezing at the surface converts the snow into snow-ice, called *névé* or *firn*. The compression of the *névé* by the addition of further layers of snow turns the lower layers into ice. When the accumulated snow and ice reaches a thickness of 200 to 300 feet (some glaciers are as much as 3,000 feet thick), the bottom layers of ice become plastic under the immense weight of the upper layers, and whole mass begins to move downwards, until higher temperatures farther down the mountain melt it to a halt. The melt-water is released bit by bit and flows down the valleys in glacial streams that merge with one another until ultimately they join the rivers far below.

When we came closer to Communism Peak, I could see the grey moraines along the sides of the Fedchenko Glacier. They were the signs of the glacier's progress down the mountainside, as it tears away rocks and earth from the valley walls. It occurred to me that if one could, by some magic, compress time so that years became minutes, one would see the glaciers flowing down the mountain valleys like rivers. The

Filled by melt-water from the ice-packed mountains, the Blue Lake, set at 15,000 feet in the western Pamirs, catches the evening light.

glacial lakes would appear and disappear as they alternately melted and froze with the seasons, changing from pinpricks of vivid blue, as I saw them now, to vacant patches of ice lost in the snowy wilderness around them. If centuries rather than years were reduced to minutes, the whole ocean of the Pamirs would begin to move, for these are young mountains still in the process of formation. In the past 10,000 years, according to a study carried out by a Soviet geographer in 1971, they have risen by over 2,000 feet, adding an average of $2\frac{1}{2}$ inches a year to their height. As we flew on, I could imagine the icy waves below sinking and rising in response to the tectonic forces at work in the earth's crust as the wedge of India passes farther and farther under Central Asia.

These tectonic movements can have remarkably sudden effects on mountain topography. As we neared the end of our flight, my neighbour pointed out a large expanse of dark blue water cupped in the mountains. It was Lake Sarez, he said, which had begun to form literally overnight in February 1911. A shift in the terrain dislodged an entire mountainside which slid downhill and formed a 500-foot-high wall of rock across a river valley. Melt-water built up behind it to create the lake. Villagers below the new lake still live in fear that some day the dam might burst.

Shortly afterwards, we landed at the small airport of Khorog, 15 miles outside the town, and set out into the high mountains. My first objective was to see a glacial river at close quarters, and so complete my task of tracing the waters of Turkestan. We hired the Soviet version of a jeep and drove 30 miles north to a spectacular fissure I had heard about where the melt-water of the river Bartang, whose name means "narrow crack", plunges through the mountains. This almost impassable valley is famous for its perilous *ovrings*—a local word for "foothold"—which can be anything from narrow ledges high up on the rock face to mere handgrips that allow a man to crawl along a sheer wall, fly-fashion, above the roaring stream.

Though this was only recently established, the Bartang is probably the only river that crosses the entire Pamirs from east to west, flowing down with many name changes from the borders of China until it joins the Piandzh, a source tributary of the Amu Darya, at Rushan on the Afghan border. We left the jeep in Rushan, obtained a guide and started on what proved to be an arduous hike up the "narrow crack". I have to admit that at first we had little idea of the scale of our undertaking. It seemed we would be heading in the direction of Lake Sarez, even though I knew full well that no one could hike all the way to the lake without

*Towards the top of the Bartang Canyon in the western Pamirs, walls of slate and granite (top) alternate with scree-littered banks (above). This valley has been gouged out by the melt-water that during the summer months turns the spring trickle seen here to floods foaming down to the Amu Darya.*

long preparation. However, that knowledge soon paled to nothing in comparison with our immediate problems. I had been told that the only way to go up the Bartang was on foot. What I did not know was that I really needed more than two feet. Even an octopus would find the walk demanding. Imagine almost sheer rock walls, hundreds—sometimes thousands—of feet high, with a narrow, roaring stream snaking along the bottom. In some places, not many, there were stretches of pebbly ground between the water and the rock face, never more than two or three feet wide, but just enough to walk on. In other places we had to step from one slippery rock to another amidst the swirling water.

It was still early spring and the glaciers had not yet begun to release their full torrential strength. By May, we were told, the water would be rushing in a solid flood from wall to wall. Then the only way of moving up the canyon would be by the *ovrings*. As we stumbled uphill, it was easy to imagine what an impressive sight the Bartang would be then. The rock walls had been worn smooth by water and whirling rocks over millenia of glacial floods, and were naked of vegetation except for a few tough trees that clung miraculously to the cliff faces. Each year this residual greenery is given a brutal test by the river, but when the water subsides, it is still there, apparently unharmed.

Our progress was marked by numerous waterfalls cascading in transparent curtains from overhanging crags and losing themselves noisily in heaps of rocks at the bottom. After a while the canyon widened, but the scenery became if possible more ascetic: scree slopes littered with pieces of rock so rectangular that they might have been quarried; giant, gaunt boulders resting at haphazard angles upon smaller stones; great plates of slate formed by the intense compression of the Pamirs long ago and tipped up on end like chimneys against the sky. Very occasionally the Cubist landscape was relieved by Pre-Raphaelite glimpses of cosy little riverside meadows, sheltered in narrow creeks. After about three miles, however, the novelty of walking in a glacial riverbed began to pall. I was drenched and my shoes were falling apart. I am an adventurous type—I spent my youth tramping over the Siberian tundra—but the Bartang crack was, as far as I was concerned, strictly for cockroaches. "How far do you think we should go?" I asked the guide testily.

"Oh," the man answered breezily, "I can go for days. How far do you want to go?"

We found a reasonably dry rock and sat down to consider matters. I don't know if any explorer has followed the Bartang along its entire course across the Pamirs, or even as far as Lake Sarez, so there was an element of challenge in our situation. But we had neither the equipment nor the time for such a journey.

"Of course," the guide continued, "in a few days the water will begin to rise and everything will be washed away." These arguments clinched matters. We gave up and turned back. In any case, we asked ourselves by way of a morale booster, what on earth could keep anyone in this utterly inhospitable wilderness?

As we finally approached the road at Rushan, we were unexpectedly given an answer. We met an old man riding a sturdy, long-haired pony. His face resembled a baked apple and his eyes were mere slits: the result of life-long exposure to the strong sun of the mountains, where there is less atmosphere to filter the ultra-violet rays. It was impossible to determine his age, but he must have been very old. On his arm was a large eagle, the bird mountain people use for hunting in preference to falcons. The eagle had a felt cap over its head so that it would not be distracted until its master sent it after its prey. Attached to the old man's saddle was a rolled fish-net, an item of equipment that baffled me.

The old man spoke only the local language and we conversed with him through a small Tadzhik boy who had appeared out of nowhere with the suddenness that always surprises me about the mountain people; it turned out that the boy had a little rudimentary Russian (he would have learned it at school, since Russian is the state language and is taught throughout the Soviet Union). No, the old man said through our interpreter, he was not going fishing. He used the net to catch snow leopards. He would throw it over the big cat and, as it thrashed around, it would wrap itself up "like a baby in swaddling clothes".

The old man told us that he lived all alone, high in the mountains. He had had three wives, but all of them were dead. His five sons were living somewhere "on the flat land". One of them was "a big teacher" in Samarkand, and he wanted his father to come and live with him. But the old man did not want to leave the mountains. When we asked him why, he squinted at the snow-covered peaks for a few seconds. "They are free," he said, "and they are clean."

The old man clicked his tongue and started off, leaving me thinking. Certainly the mountains were clean. There were no scattered eggshells here, no empty tins and bottles, no crumpled newspapers. People do not go picnicking among ice-covered cliffs. But the greatest advantage must surely be the freedom. To anyone and anything that can endure the hardship of this frozen wilderness, the mountains offer a sanctuary.

*The snow leopard is perfectly adapted to life in the high Pamirs and Tien Shan mountains, its only known habitat apart from the Himalayas. Inhabiting rarefied altitudes of up to 20,000 feet, it is kept warm by long, feathery fur that covers a dense, woolly undercoat. It can run at up to 50 m.p.h.—a speed that enables it to ensnare the yak calves and mountain sheep it needs for food.*

"In that kingdom of narrow paths," wrote Marco Polo, "are many inaccessible places, so that the dwellers therein have no fear of the foe." In the past, the Tadzhiks found freedom in the Pamirs from conquerors, local khans, landlords, tax collectors and other oppressors. Today a few hardened individuals like the old man with the eagle still live in the lonely *kishlaks*, the tiny mountain settlements often tucked away only just below the permanent snow-line, and clearly they cherish their isolation from modern civilization.

On the way back to Khorog, our interest in wild places recovered sufficiently for us to plan the next stage of our travels. Clearly, to cross the entire Pamirs from east to west, we would have to travel by some way other than the Bartang canyon. The only practical route through this forbidding country is the Khorog—Kyzylart highway, which contains three high mountain passes. It is part of the ancient Silk Route connecting medieval Europe with the riches of India, Tibet and China. Caravans of up to 2,000 camels and horses once passed this way, laden with silks and spices. For centuries the caravan leaders, who were said to require at least 30 years' experience before they mastered the art of balancing and securing the loads, took their valuable animal trains up the precipitous passes, across glaciers and through mountain streams with hardly a lost consignment, singing songs that were as long and as melancholy as the route. We did not expect such problems, but there are sections of the road where the caravaners' warning still applies: "Traveller, beware! Here thou art as a tear on an eyelash!"

Apart from the vague sense of excitement one often feels when treading in the footsteps of long-dead pioneers, there was a strong geographical attraction in our route. We would be scaling the eastern wall of Turkestan, part of the mighty complex of mountains that keeps the moist winds from the deserts and divides the palaearctic zone of animal life—all Russia and Europe—from the oriental, which includes India, China and the Malay peninsula. There are great scenic contrasts between east and west and also, as anyone seeking to understand mountains must realize, between the various heights. To pass from one level to another is like travelling through different countries, only here the changes are arranged vertically rather than horizontally.

As we drove eastwards in our jeep I was struck first of all by the sharp cut and thrust of the landscape. The gigantic peaks of the western Pamirs soared up above us, making us feel totally insignificant. We crawled like ants through sombre canyons filled with the sound of roaring streams. As we climbed, I began to get a better idea of the four levels of the Pamirs: the valleys, the highlands, the lower peaks and the high peaks.

In the steep-sided valleys, at about 7,500 to 9,000 feet above sea level, the vegetation was sparse. Although maples, wild walnuts, pistachios and almonds, wild apples and pear trees grow on this side of the mountains, we saw only the ubiquitous juniper, the long-lived trees that make up half the Pamir woodlands. Because these junipers' extensive root systems must be able to capture sufficient surface moisture, they must grow well apart from one another, creating very thin, open woods.

At the end of this first level—at 12,000 to 13,000 feet—was the snow-line. The ground was strewn with broken stones, the moraines of former glaciers, and gouged by round holes, known as cirques, filled with ice or water. Gnarled shrubs hugged the cold ground; otherwise the rock was bare. As we passed the snow-line at the top of our first pass, I noticed that my companions were finding breathing difficult in the rarefied air, though I seemed to be all right myself. I was nevertheless relieved when we breasted the pass and descended to the valley of the river Gunt, another tributary of the Piandzh. We stopped for refreshment at a solitary tea house. As we drank our tea, we got into conversation with a lorry driver who was on his way to deliver a transistor radio and some tinned food to a nearby *kishlak* where he had relatives. Of course, he added, the road stops short several miles below the settlement, and even that is a dirt track. His relatives would have to come down to meet him there. He paused. "Come to think of it, why don't you go back up with them? Then you would see the real Pamirs."

"Wouldn't it be a difficult climb?" I asked cautiously.

"Oh, not at all," the man said breezily. "Anywhere a yak can go, you can."

Now, wait a minute, I thought. I am pretty strong for my age, but there is a point where flattery becomes useless. I was very well aware that I could not keep up with a full-grown yak in good physical condition. As a child I knew some of them intimately when I was travelling in Mongolia with my father. They are formidable looking brutes with great curved horns and long hair almost reaching to the ground. Their amazing stability and agility enable them to negotiate trails that seem impassable to anyone but mountaineers, treating wide cracks and jumbles of boulders with as little concern as a tarmac road. Their legs are like pneumatic jacks and scissors combined, just folding under at the front to go up a step, staying down while the back legs find a purchase and then, with a powerful heave, lifting up.

"Oh, come," the man insisted. "You can't miss a chance to see the real mountains."

This was tempting and no doubt, instead of matching my prowess against a yak, I might be able to get a ride and let it do the climbing. Somewhat reluctantly, I agreed.

About two hours later we were jolting up a rough dirt road with me half-lying in the back of the lorry between cardboard boxes. I was getting cramp and thinking fitfully about yaks. I knew that the Gunt River valley was real yak country, and that here yaks were an all important part of the economy. They are often compared to the llama of the Andes for their economic significance, but the comparison is not accurate. One cannot milk a llama or use it as a saddle animal. The yak, on the other hand, can supply virtually all the needs of the mountain people: transport, milk and milk products, meat, leather, wool and also fuel (its droppings are used for building fires in the treeless high mountains). The local saying has it that "the yak is to the Pamir what a camel is to the desert—the best gift of Allah to a mountain Tadzhik."

The lorry came to an abrupt halt. "We have arrived," the driver announced. "The road goes no farther."

As I got out, I saw a small, pebbly river and beyond it a long slope dotted with cattle and a snow-capped mountain in the background. The air, I noticed, was distinctly cold. We must have climbed a long way.

On the other side of the river, a bevy of children ran forward to greet us. Three or four were riding on a large, oxen-like animal that turned out to be a yak. Presumably the "cattle" in the distance were also yaks. Several old men cantered up on some more yaks, and a moment later the whole party forded the shallow stream and rode up to us, sitting well back and leaning on a single rope threaded through the yaks' noses. The air was thick with the sour smell of damp yak, and we were showered with drops of water as the animals shook themselves dry. The men and children slid down from their mounts. There was a good deal of talking that I could not understand. Men were embracing and kissing our driver—the usual procedure in all Muslim countries.

The men began loading the cardboard boxes from the back of the lorry on to their animals. Each owner kept his yak still by placing his thumb and middle fingers in her nostrils and keeping a firm hold ("her" because yak bulls are hardly manageable, and are never used as pack or saddle animals). This method seemed to work well: though they grunted and rolled their bulging brown eyes dolefully, the yaks submitted calmly while the loads were secured on their backs with stout ropes woven from their own hair. Very strong ropes they were too, I was told.

Meanwhile, a carpet had materialized on the ground and the usual *dastarkhan* or food offering for guests was spread out on it: thick yak yoghurt, yak cheese and flat oatmeal bread, the traditional Pamir mountain food. We broke off pieces of bread and scooped out the yoghurt with it—quite tasty.

I had to converse with my hosts, all old men, only through the driver. "They want you to come and sleep in their *kishlak* tonight," he told me.

"How far is it?" I asked.

"Not far," the driver said. "Maybe 10-15-20 kilometres." (Vagueness about distances is characteristic of mountain people.) "It is a cultured place," he continued. "They have radios, a school and a club-house."

I looked at the glistening white mountain in the distance. In between there was a frightening switchback up a nearly vertical rock face. If I accepted, I would have to go up it.

"How would I get there?"

"On one of the yaks. She is a good saddle animal. You try her," the driver assured me.

I was tempted. In my younger days I was a good rider. I rode camels in Egypt. Once I tried, disastrously, to ride an ostrich—in the Ukraine, of all places. (Ostriches were brought to the Ukraine by an eccentric Russian nature-lover 100 years ago and have thrived there ever since.) But it was many years since I had been on a yak. There was a good deal of conversation among the Tadzhiks, and then one of the boys brought up a very large black and white beast with a flat wooden saddle and a single rein threaded through her nostrils, as I had noticed earlier.

"She belongs to my grandfather," the lorry driver said proudly. "A real *shaitan*."

The word *shaitan* means "devil", but it is used very loosely in the mountains. Any good, sturdy animal would be described as a *shaitan*. Meanwhile all the Tadzhiks were on their feet, watching me with their infectious smiles, and I knew I was trapped. I had to ride a yak.

With the help of a few men I climbed on. The saddle was surprisingly comfortable. The driver pushed the rope into my hands and said something which I did not fully understand: "She sees food—she eats. Don't stop her. There is little enough up in the mountains."

Before I could ask exactly what he meant, a small boy hit the animal's flank with a stone out of his herder's sling and the brute broke into a sort of jogging trot towards the river. Her motion was easy and her back stayed surprisingly level. I was greatly encouraged, and quite proud of myself. The Tadzhiks shouted and applauded. I was becoming a hero.

We forded the stream and started up the slope on the outer side. I stayed on my mount. I was beginning to feel as relaxed as a true yak *djigit*, or a "rough rider". We had covered perhaps 100 yards (I say "we" though the animal was in sole charge since I did not know what to do with the rope) when suddenly, without the slightest warning, the animal abruptly changed her course. There was a violent forwards and downwards lurch, and I went rolling head over heels on the ground.

For a moment I was stunned. When I got up shakily, I saw my yak peacefully devouring a succulent tuft of grass nearby. Now I understood what the driver had said. Being a ruminant animal, capable of cropping food and chewing it later, the yak wastes no chance of a likely mouthful. I would probably have done the same had I been a yak cow.

"In two or three years you will ride like a real *djigit*," the driver told me. "Everybody falls the first 10-20-30 times."

Meanwhile there was a spirited conference among my Tadzhik friends. Generally I like being among people whose language I cannot understand: it spares one a great deal of nonsense. But now I was anxious. Obviously my fate was being discussed, since the men continually pointed their fingers in my direction. Finally the driver turned to me. He looked embarrassed.

"They say, maybe you had better come in winter when there is no grass."

"Wonderful!" I said with feeling. "Please thank them. I'll be happy to come and stay."

That was the end of that episode. After my exertions, I was beginning to shiver. It was now intensely cold, and would be much colder still up in the *kishlak*. The snowy summits of the mountains seemed to breathe an icy, death-like stillness. The view was glorious, but the desolation was overpowering. I have seen many wild places in my time, but the thought of life up in the *kishlak*, I must confess, rather shocked me.

The price of freedom in the mountain sanctuary is a high one. First of all, there is the terrible isolation. Until recently people living in neighbouring valleys spoke different dialects, and did not know of one another's existence. Even today, despite transistor radios, the *kishlak* dwellers must adapt themselves to the constant loneliness of life with the snow and the sky. Now that the young people are leaving for the valleys and cities, those who remain must face the addi-

*Snow-capped peaks and wind-whipped frozen sand mark the highest pass in the Pamirs, located at 13,000 feet near Lake Karakul.*

tional spectre of a lonely old age. Then there is the sheer physical hardship. An economy based on the yak, with perhaps a few sheep and a little hunting, provides an extremely meagre livelihood.

At last we were ready to leave. Several of the old men kissed me. "They say, come and live with them," the driver interpreted. "It is a good life in the mountains. Good air, good sun, and not too many officials. You are old; in the mountains people die happy." This time I was not tempted. The return of civilization, even in the form of the lorry's hard wooden floor, was a delightful anticipation. I was keen to be going.

On our way again towards the eastern Pamirs, I was able to get some insights into other animals' adaptations to the high mountain environment. We saw long-tailed marmots almost everywhere, darting away between rocks, and when we followed them to one of their colonies, we counted literally hundreds of burrows. The little rodents sat on their haunches, and filled the air with a peculiar whistling, probably a warning signal. These rodents are well suited to the cold, since they can hibernate in their very deep burrows for nine months of the year.

Here was an example of an animal exploiting the mountain habitat by its ability to withstand hardship. The other animals of the high Pamirs, including bears, snow leopards, eagles and mountain goats, all have some way of mitigating the cold. Bears hibernate (as do the marmots). Sheep and goats move up and down the mountainside with the changing seasons. Birds, noticeably the huge black griffins, migrate. One thing we particularly noticed is that animals like the markhor mountain goat and the Marco Polo sheep grow to enormous sizes; the Pamir bears are among the largest in the world. The reason for this is that the largest animals have the smallest surface area in proportion to mass, so that they lose less of their body heat into the air. Consequently, over many millenia, the animals with the evolutionary advantage of great size in a cold climate have attained a noticeable predominance.

As we entered the eastern Pamirs the scene changed dramatically. Instead of saw-toothed peaks and narrow canyons, we moved among mountains with more rounded contours and wide, open valleys. The landscape had a much more lifeless look about it. There were no trees, and about the only plants we did find were tucked away in sheltered ravines: a few Siberian primroses and some mountain onions with leaves covered in a fine fur to keep out the cold. Apart from this there was nothing but rocks, rocks, rocks, decorated here and there with low "cushion" plants of sombre colours varying from dark green to a dull violet. There is less precipitation here than anywhere else in Soviet Central Asia, including the arid Karakum and Kyzylkum deserts: 2.4 inches a year at Murgab and one inch at Lake Karakul. We were, in fact, passing through what one could justly call a mountain desert.

It was at Karakul, one of the highest lakes in the world, that I encountered the most astonishing phenomenon of this extraordinary trip. From a distance the lake appeared as a huge black spot among the mountains—in keeping with its name, which means Black Lake. But when we came closer we were amazed to see that it was surrounded by typical desert sand dunes. When we got out of the jeep for a few minutes, we found that the strong wind was driving frozen sand into our faces.

From here we followed the ancient Silk Route north towards our final goal of Kirgizia and the Tien Shan mountains, another wilderness even less known and explored than the Pamirs. For mile after mile we saw no signs of life, until we came to the desolate Markansu Valley. Not far from the road lay the bodies of horses and camels, perfectly preserved by the frosty, arid air. They were the mummified relics of caravans that passed this way long ago, a grisly reminder of the harshness of the high mountains we were in.

# Rivers of Ice

High up in the knotted and snowy ranges of the Pamirs and Tien Shan mountains lie some of the greatest glaciers on earth outside the Antarctic. These glaciers coat a combined area of over 13,000 square miles, and one of them—the Fedchenko Glacier in the Pamirs—is 43 miles long. These massive tongues of ice, originally formed during the Ice Age of 10,000 years or more ago, and sustained by regular falls of snow that turn into compressed layers, seem at first glance to be inert. But they are, in fact, in continuous motion, gouging out valleys and flattening obstructions.

Once a snow- or ice-field in a sloping mountain valley is 200 or 300 feet thick, the lowest levels give under the great weight of accumulated ice and begin to move downwards, carrying with them the brittle mass above. As the glacier moves over the irregular gradients of the valley floor, it is wracked by tensions and strains and constantly cracks open into crevasses and fissures.

Covering a few inches or a few feet a day, the ice churns up the valley floor and dislodges rock from the walls, creating monumental cargoes of debris, or "moraines", which build up underneath it, disfigure its borders and collect at its front end or "snout". As the glacier grinds its way down, sweeping the moraines along with it, it constantly reshapes the landscape.

Sometimes the glacier's movement is not all that slow. The Medvezhy, or Bear Glacier, in the Pamirs, illustrated on the following pages, is at nine miles long a dwarf among its neighbours. Yet what it lacks in size it makes up for in activity. On April 22, 1963, it went on a sudden rampage down the Vanch Valley. With a grinding roar that sent panic-stricken villagers fleeing for safety, it lunged forward for over a mile before coming to rest.

As a glacier moves down the mountain, reaching warmer levels— the temperature rises by up to five degrees for every thousand feet—it begins to melt, spreading out and exposing an ever greater area to the sun's heat. It drops its debris and breaks into an icy sweat as countless rivulets begin to flow across its face. Cascading through blue-green chasms, overflowing countless pools, or pouring in murky torrents through the terminal moraine, the melt-water of the Medvezhy runs down to make glacial lakes, or flows on to join one of the rivers of Turkestan.

*The Medvezhy Glacier at the start of its downward journey piles over a sharp slope in ultra slow-motion to form an ice-fall. The broad gashes in the snow (centre and foreground) are crevasses opened by enormous tensions in the brittle ice as the lowest levels of the glacier pass over the uneven valley floor. Widest at their centres and tapering to cracks at the sides, crevasses are often hundreds of feet deep and hung with giant icicles.*

Twisted pinnacles of ice up to 30 feet high rise from the surface of the glacier in jumbled confusion. These "seracs", photographed near the snout after the glacier has reached a temperate zone, are formed during a process called ablation whereby the ice rapidly melts and collapses under the dual onslaught of the sun's heat and the dryness of the continental winds.

Moving down the valley like a river— the middle flowing faster than the sides and the surface faster than the ground layers—the Medvezhy assumes a tongue-like shape. Its leading edge is cloaked with an ugly mantle of rocks, boulders and dust known as the terminal moraine, which has accumulated from avalanches and the debris eroded from the valley walls.

*A flotilla of ice chunks lies becalmed in a giant pool that has collected just in front of the glacier's melting and crumbling snout.*

*Melt-water from the glacier rushes down a stepped valley, breaking into waterfalls.*

In the lower glacial valley, well below the snout of the glacier, a muddy lake forms from melt-water loaded with sediment. Erosion on the steep mountainside below the glacier is generally severe, as the stark surroundings of the lake bear witness. Scree or stony slopes build up as boulders and debris rattle downhill from higher cliffs after being released by the melting snows in spring.

# 6/ Conquerors of the Heights

*No place in the world has been surrounded by such a thick veil of mystery and none has been so difficult of access for centuries.*

WILLIAM E. CURTIS/ *TURKESTAN, THE HEART OF ASIA*

So wild and impenetrable had the Pamirs and Tien Shan appeared to me, that I knew that were it not for aeroplanes, cars and good maps I would never have had the temerity to venture into them at all. It was not difficult therefore to realize that little more than a century earlier, these mountains were scarcely more than large blanks on the maps of Central Asia. It was virtually *terra incognita*, into which few foreigners ever ventured. But slowly, through the 19th Century, European explorers, mostly Russian and British, began to trickle into these remote areas, seeking knowledge either for its own sake or for strategic reasons.

The Pamirs were the first of these two mountain barriers to be explored, for they straddled the potentially sensitive border area between the empires of Russia and British India. They were also the more accessible. And there was something at least known of them from the few travellers who had passed through them in previous centuries. The Pamirs had long exercised a fascination, for it was believed that the mighty Oxus had its source in these mountains and the river, then considered a cradle of civilization, had figured in the literature and geography of many successive cultures.

In the 5th and 6th Centuries A.D., Chinese Buddhist priests had crossed the Pamirs in their search for Buddhist scriptures in India. The most successful of these Chinese pilgrims was Hwen Tsang, who journeyed for 16 years and returned to China with 22 horse-loads of

Buddhist literature. He later compiled his *Records of the Western World*, in which he described his travels in the Pamirs. He had seen, he wrote plaintively, neither men nor villages, "encountering nothing but ice and snow. The snow falls both in summer and spring-time. Night and day the wind rages violently".

For six more centuries no other traveller wrote of these remote regions. Then, in the late 13th Century, the Venetian merchant, Marco Polo, crossed the Pamirs on his epic journey to the court of Kublai Khan in China. He approached the mountains from present-day Afghanistan in the south-west. "When you . . . ride three days north-east, always among mountains," he wrote, "you get to such a height that it is said to be the highest place in the world. The region is so lofty and cold that you do not see any birds flying," and then—in an uncomprehending description of the lack of oxygen at high altitudes—"because of this great cold, fire does not burn so brightly, nor give out so much heat as usual, nor does it cook food so effectually." He went on to describe the huge sheep later named after him: "there are great numbers of all kinds of wild beasts, among others, wild sheep of great size, having horns, three, four, and even six palms in length," from which the shepherds made "ladles and vessels for holding their victuals" and "fences. for enclosing their cattle, and securing them against the wolves, with which they say the country is infested." In Europe, reports of the giant sheep were scorned and helped to earn Marco Polo the nickname of "Il Milione"—"The Million"—the story-teller whose many fantastic tales could outdo *One Thousand and One Nights*.

For the next 600 years little was added to the meagre store of recorded knowledge on the Pamirs. At the beginning of the 19th Century, Shelley could still write of them as

*. . . Aerial mountains which pour down*
*Indus and Oxus from their icy caves . . .*

for they were still part of legend. The situation was, however, about to change. The areas in which these two rivers had their sources had begun to intrigue the governments of Russia and Britain as their empires expanded towards each other. In 1836 Britain dispatched Lieutenant John Wood of the Indian Navy to explore the Indus River and the lands through which its headwaters flowed, and to collect on his way any information of commercial and military value.

From the Indus Wood continued northwards through Afghanistan into the Pamirs, searching for the source of the Oxus. He followed one of its main headstreams, the Piandzh, along much of the same route probably taken centuries before by Marco Polo. Finally, after days of climbing and hardship, in the afternoon of February 19, 1838, Wood arrived on the "Roof of the World", and found the headstream of the Piandzh issuing from a "noble but frozen sheet of water"—Lake Zorkul.

"The aspect of the landscape was wintry in the extreme," he later recalled in ringing Victorian phrases. " . . . not a beast, not even a bird, was visible. The sound of a human voice would have been music to the ear, but no one at this inhospitable season thinks of invading these gelid domains. Silence reigned around—silence so profound that it oppressed the heart, and, as I contemplated the hoary summits of the everlasting mountains, where human foot had never trod, and where lay piled the snows of ages, my own dear country and all the social blessings it contains passed across my mind with a vividness of recollection that I had never felt before."

One native inhabitant of the Pamirs particularly intrigued Wood: the yak, or the "kash-gow" as he called it. "Yaks are gregarious, and set the wolves, which here abound, at defiance," he wrote. "Where a man can walk, a kash-gow may be ridden."

Wood also described the yak's supposed method of eating by removing the snow from the grass. "If the snow on the elevated flats lies too deep for him to crop the herbiage, he rolls himself down the slopes and eats his way up again. When he arrives at the top, he performs a second summerset [somersault] and completes his meal, as he displaces another groove of snow in his second ascent." The yak is a marvellous animal, but it certainly does not use this ingenious somersaulting method of feeding as a regular practice and I suspect that the romantic Lieutenant Wood was retailing local folk-tales.

On the other hand, Wood did make a firm contribution to science by providing the evidence that won scientific acceptance for the giant sheep earlier reported by Marco Polo. Wood wrote of seeing "numbers of horns strewed about in every direction," some of them "of an astonishingly large size," belong to an "animal of a species between goat and sheep." He dispatched a set of horns to Europe, and the sheep was henceforth known as the *Ovis poli*, "Polo's sheep."

In the 1860s came the first Russian approach to the Pamirs, by the naturalist-explorer, Fedchenko, who had no motive other than the acquisition of knowledge. "More is known about the moon than the Pamirs," he lamented. Fedchenko penetrated only as far as the Trans-Alai range, the ridge north of the Pamirs, and he died soon after this expedition. But he made some valuable studies—a glacier, thought until

This view of the summer remnants of a Pamirs glacier was drawn by Olga Fedchenko, wife of one of the area's greatest explorers.

recently to be the largest in the world is named after him—and his explorations were soon followed by a full Russian military expedition. A detachment of this group, complete with a geographer, geodesist, natural historian and topographer, reached Lake Karakul, which no European had seen in modern times.

The detachment's geographer, a Captain Kostenko, duly reported on the azure lake and the "great number of water-fowl skimming the surface." So cold and rarefied was the air on the heights around Karakul that many of the men bled from the nose and several fainted. But Kostenko did not suffer from mountain sickness and reported contemptuously that the sufferers were "doubtless those who are accustomed to spirituous liquors".

The British, on their side, continued the exploration begun by Wood. In 1873, Lieutenant T. E. Gordon reached Wood's lake. Gordon was fascinated by the big-horned Marco Polo sheep. A pair of horns Gordon presented to the British Museum measured $65\frac{1}{2}$ inches in length round the curve, 53 inches in a straight line from tip to tip and 16 inches round the base. As for the meat of the *Ovis poli*, Gordon found it "good and pleasant to the taste, with a slight flavour of venison". It does indeed have that flavour but is much tougher.

In 1894 there arrived in the Pamirs the remarkable George Nathaniel Curzon, later to be Viceroy of India. As a result of his prolific reading about and travel in Asia, Curzon had long been intrigued by the Oxus, whose waters, he wrote, told "of forgotten peoples" and whispered "secrets of unknown lands". He was convinced that Wood had not found the true source of the river, and he wished to find it himself.

Curzon went to Wood's lake and established to his satisfaction that it was not the true source. Curzon claimed that the source was a great glacier to the south-east of Zorkul (even this was an over-simplification: a mass of small rivers and lakes contribute their waters to Zorkul). In the course of a few days in the Pamirs, Curzon wryly claimed to have undergone "the bodily labours of a Parliamentary session and parted with the superfluous physical accretions of an entire London season".

The British and the Russians were not the only explorers of these mountains. In the same year in which Curzon made his memorable study of the Pamirs, the Swede, Sven Hedin, one of the great explorers of Central Asia, crossed the mountains from the Russian side—and in winter. Braving the climate which his predecessors had found inclement enough in other seasons, Hedin and his Kirgiz guides pushed on through waist-high snow, the guides calling aloud to Allah for help in survival. Laboriously they made their way over the highlands to Karakul and to the Russian outpost beyond. Here Hedin was hospitably received by the Russian commander, who courteously drank to the health of Oscar, King of Sweden and Norway. "If ever a toast was responded to with real sincerity and gratitude," recalled Hedin, "it was when I stood up to return thanks for the honour done to my King. If ever there was a place where joy reigned supreme, it was surely here on the Roof of the World, 11,850 feet above the level of the sea, far removed from the bustle and noise of the busy world, in the very middle of Asia—a region where our nearest neighbours were the wild sheep of the mountain crags, the wolves which prowl over the snowy wastes, the imperial eagle which soars through the endless spaces of the sky."

By the end of the 19th Century the Pamirs had been fairly well explored. As Hedin himself acknowledged—perhaps a trifle sadly—the white patches on the map were gradually disappearing. "The pioneers will soon have played their part . . . The pioneers of the past, who cleared the way through increasing danger and difficulty, have been followed by the explorers of the present day, examining in detail the surface of the earth and its restless life."

Even the Tien Shan range, the vast natural bastion to the north-east of the Pamirs, which stretches 1,500 miles from present-day Soviet Kirgizia into Chinese Sinkiang, was no longer inviolate. Local tribesmen called these once inaccessible, eternally snow-clad summits Tengri-tag, or "Mountains of the Spirits". The Chinese had translated the phrase as Tien Shan—the "Celestial Mountains"—and the name stuck. The first European to penetrate the Tien Shan was a man of extraordinary ability and achievement: Peter Semyonov, one of the greatest explorers of the 19th Century (though little known outside Russia). He combined the expert qualities of a soldier, geographer, geologist, zoologist, mineralogist, botanist, surveyor, ethnologist, administrator and art connoisseur.

Semyonov was born in 1827 into the landed gentry, but although he received a traditional education in a military academy and at the University of St. Petersburg, he dreamed of a career in geography. At 22 he joined the Russian Geographical Society (the fourth association of its kind in the world after those of London, Paris and Berlin), which put him to work translating into Russian the early volumes of the German geographer Karl Ritter's monumental 18-volume *Geography of Asia and Africa*. Ritter, then aged 80, was the founder of modern geography together with his contemporary compatriot, Alexander von Humboldt.

*George Nathaniel Curzon's haughty single-mindedness—as an undergraduate he was nicknamed "a most superior person"—served him well as an explorer. He ignored a permanent back injury to explore the source of the Oxus on the Indo-Afghan border, and he wrote up his findings so meticulously that Britain's Royal Geographical Society awarded him its gold medal.*

Humboldt, a naturalist, traveller and statesman, shared Ritter's interest in the central Asian mountains. Both were convinced that they were of volcanic origin. Studying Ritter, Semyonov became fascinated with this hypothesis and resolved to test it.

The sudden death of his first wife interrupted Semyonov's translation of Ritter. To forget his grief he plunged into preparations for his explorations in the Tien Shan. He went to Berlin, enrolled at the University, attended lectures by the great Ritter himself and discussed with him the mysteries of unexplored Asia, particularly the Celestial Mountains. He also met Humboldt, who gave his blessing to Semyonov's enterprise and told him he would indeed die happy if Semyonov were to bring him some samples of volcanic rock from the Tien Shan.

Semyonov trained for his venture by climbing in the Alps. And since he agreed with Humboldt that traces of volcanic activity would be found in the Tien Shan, he went to study a volcano at first hand: he "climbed Vesuvius 17 times from all sides, and on several occasions descended into the crater when it was filled with smoke." Finally, in 1856, with the backing of the Russian Geographical Society, Semyonov went to what is now called Alma-Ata to begin his long and historic mission to the Celestial Mountains. (Alma-Ata, "Mother of Apples", in the Kazakh language, was so named after the Revolution. Until then it was known as "Verny" or "Faithful" and was a small garrison town. Today Alma-Ata is a modern industrial city of 750,000.)

With a Cossack guard, he rode into the Kungey-Alatau range, an offshoot of the Tien Shan. As his group mounted the crest, a gigantic range came into view. "I saw for the first time," he wrote, "on the distant horizon, in the glint of the sun's rays, what for many years had been the object of my thoughts and aspirations—the unbroken, snowy chain of the Tien Shan." He then descended the south side of the Kungey-Alatau, rode through mountain steppe to the shores of Lake Issyk-Kul and returned to Alma-Ata, pleased to have accomplished his first objective: seeing the Tien Shan range in all its outward glory. Through the winter he classified and recorded the many plants, flowers, grasses and rock specimens he had brought back, and he reported to the Geographical Society his scientific, economic and political observations.

In June 1857, when the snows in the foothills had melted, Semyonov left Alma-Ata to begin his first attempt to penetrate the heart of the Tien Shan. He now had an escort of 50 Cossacks which was later joined by a detachment of a further 1,500 men. The little army climbed the Santash

*Peter Semyonov, portrayed here in his baggy-trousered Kirgiz exploring gear complete with geologist's hammer and collecting bag, was the first European to explore the Tien Shan. So assiduous was his work as explorer and collector that the Tsar bestowed on him the title Tien-Shansky—"of the Tien Shan"— a name still borne by his family.*

Pass—the Pass of the Counted Stones—which, according to legend, Tamerlane had crossed on an eastward-bound campaign. The name has an interesting origin: in order to count his losses, Tamerlane had ordered each soldier to pick up a stone from the shores of Lake Issyk-Kul and to cast it on a pile in the pass. When the army returned each surviving soldier took a stone from the pile; the stones left told Tamerlane how many men he had lost; and the lonely pile stood for posterity as a monument to his dead.

From the top of Santash a magnificent view of the main range of the snow-clad Tien Shan suddenly unfurled before Semyonov. The party began to penetrate the Tien Shan range, crossing rivers and filing down river gorges overgrown with barberries and honeysuckle, sweetbrier and clematis. Farther on, Semyonov and a small escort began the ascent towards the centre of the range. The narrow trail steepened. The vegetation became sparse and the air thin. The party began to come across the bodies of local tribesmen and animals—horses, rams and camels—prostrated where death had overtaken them and preserved by the icy mountain air. At one point Semyonov's horse, frightened at the sight of a corpse, shied and nearly plunged down a precipice. Shortly afterwards one of the pack-horses fell thousands of feet into the abyss below.

At last Semyonov reached the top of a pass so high that the foothills now appeared as an undulating plain, dotted with green lakes only partly covered by ice. It was the highest point they had reached—well above 15,000 feet. The expedition now descended on the south of the main range, crossing the alpine meadows thickly strewn with blue and yellow gentians, pale blue ranunculi and white and golden buttercups. The explorers also found broad glades covered with the golden heads of an unclassified species of onion, shortly to be named after Semyonov (*Allium semenovi*). Semyonov later learned that onions were so widespread here that the Chinese had given this part of the Tien Shan the name Tsun lin, or "onion mountains".

Instead of moving farther south, Semyonov retraced his steps back over the range and turned eastwards towards the Chinese border which ran through the mountains. On June 26 he came suddenly upon a view of what seemed the highest peaks of the range. To right and left, Semyonov counted no less than 30 snow-capped giants. Highest of them all towered Khan Tengri, the "Lord of the Spirits". (In Semyonov's day Khan Tengri, at 23,616 feet, was considered the highest peak of the Tien Shan; not until 1943 did a Soviet expedition discover a higher mountain, 15 miles south of Khan Tengri, rising to 24,406 feet. They named it Pik Pobeda—

Victory Peak—in honour of the triumphs of the Red Army, then confronting the Nazis to the west.)

In the autumn Semyonov went back to Alma-Ata, determined now to assess the results of his explorations. As he came out of the mountains, he turned for a final glimpse of his now beloved Tien Shan. The sun was setting, a full moon was rising majestically, and "a little cloud of smoke indicated a forest fire in one of the gorges of the range. A dry mist had formed a transparent haze in front of the range. The snowy summits of the Talgar group still glowed roseate and seemed small, although they were perfectly clear. Sorrowfully I cast a farewell glance at the snowy highlands of Central Asia, where for many years had lain the limits of my soul's desire."

Semyonov's achievement in the Tien Shan was immense. Not only was he the first European to explore the area. He collected more than a thousand species of plants, including many hitherto unknown to scientists. He classified the layers of flora and fauna at different altitudes in the mountains. He recorded the geology and mountain structure of the northern Tien Shan, establishing, to his own disappointment, that the mountains were not volcanic in origin.

Semyonov never returned to Central Asia. On his return from the Celestial Mountains he settled down to the life of a scholar and administrator in St. Petersburg, becoming Vice President of the Russian Geographical Society in 1873 and occupying the post for 41 years, until his death in 1914. But it was not only geographical subjects that concerned him. Besides administration, the promotion of other explorers' expeditions and the compilation of geographical encyclopaedias, he fought for and supervised the first all-Russian census, immersed himself in statistical studies of different kinds, and classified 701,000 insects of Russia and Central Asia collected for him by successive explorers; these he presented to St. Petersburg's Museum of Zoology.

In 1907, on the occassion of the 50th anniversary of his journey to the Celestial Mountains, he was awarded by imperial edict of the Tsar the title of "Semyonov Tien-Shansky", or "Semyonov of the Tien Shan". By the time of his death in 1914 he had been made an honorary member of 66 academies, universities and scientific societies throughout the world. The Berlin Geographical Society awarded him the silver Karl Ritter medal—but in his case struck it in gold. His name had been given to flowers and grasses, insects, animals, glaciers and mountains.

Semyonov's link with the Tien Shan was intensified by one of his pro-

*Shown here in the dress uniform of the Russian Army, Nikolai Przhevalsky explored the far reaches of Central Asia, unveiling new desert and mountain terrain in Russia, China and Mongolia. He lies buried—according to his own instructions—on the shores of Lake Issyk-Kul, in the heart of the Tien Shan mountains he loved.*

tégés—Nikolai Przhevalsky—who was to become one of the most famous explorers of the land beyond these mountains. Przhevalsky achieved his own fame with his expeditions to Tibet and across the great deserts of Central Asia, and to the fabled lakes of Lop Nor and Koko Nor. Among Przhevalsky's more famous discoveries were the wild camel of Central Asia and a rare species of wild horse which is named after him: *Equus przhevalski*. Przhevalsky crossed the eastern Chinese Tien Shan, which Semyonov had never seen. And, at the end of his fourth expedition, he returned over the Celestial Mountains from Takla Makan in the south to Lake Issyk-Kul. Here he was suddenly taken ill and died, in 1888, while planning another expedition. His instructions were: "Bury me in my field expedition outfit on the shore of Issyk-Kul." His grave still stands there.

It would seem that the Tien Shan mountains hold no more mysteries for explorers and that this last "blank space" of Central Asia has now been filled in. But exploration of this remote and still mysterious area is far from completed and cartographers are still confused by some of the mountains. It is difficult to determine accurate topography, even from the air, through the blanket of snow and ice. The confusion over the Tien Shan's topography was put to me succinctly by an old friend, an airline pilot. As we flew over this great range, he pointed to the snow-clad peaks below, and exclaimed: "The Devil himself wouldn't be able to unscramble that frozen mess."

# A Naturalist's Challenge

The Pamir mountains, soaring up to 24,000 feet, provide one of the wildest, toughest animal habitats in Turkestan. Their mighty bulk stops the swirling Indian storms and their icy peaks shred the clouds, turning the rains to thick, suffocating carpets of snow. Above the permanent snow-line between 12,000 and 14,000 feet, very little can grow or live. Even the middle heights above 9,000 feet are harsher than the moisture-starved deserts beyond. Icy winds batter the steep slopes and temperatures drop below freezing every night of the year.

Man cannot live here for any length of time, and anyone wishing to study the high-mountain creatures and their adaptations has to endure severe hardship. The 19th-Century Russian zoologists accepted the challenge with enthusiasm, and the pictures that follow illustrate some results of their untiring research. Outstanding among these experts were Nikolai Przhevalsky, later made famous by his work in Mongolia (a rare Mongolian horse is named after him: *Equus przhevalski*) and N. V. Severtsov, who became the father of Turkestan zoology.

Severtsov spent years roaming the Pamirs in order to build up a complete picture of the animals' relationships to one another and to their environment. One of his case studies was the Himalayan vulture (opposite), which he eventually tracked to all of its seasonal habitats. Daring the swollen snow rivers and avalanches of early summer, Severtsov located the vultures' nesting place in the nearly inaccessible alpine grass zone, just below the snow at around 11,500 feet. Exploring the belt of firs and birches between 6,500 and 10,500 feet, he traced the bird to its mid-summer home, where it grew fat on kills left by bears and wolves. And finally he followed the bird down the mountains as it was driven by the winter snows to the shelter of the larch and ash zone around 6,000 feet.

Such a thorough concentration on one specimen was a departure from the normal practice of Severtsov's day. Many of his contemporaries were concerned mainly with making lists of species and then haggling over the classifications. Severtsov sacrificed personal advancement in this field for the overriding aim of getting things right: his accounts of life in the Pamirs seem more suited to modern ecology than to the science of his own era.

HIMALAYAN GRIFFON VULTURE

## Birds of High Passage

The great mountains of eastern Turkestan have held a special attraction for zoologists because they mark the border between two of the world's main faunal areas: the palaearctic to the west and oriental to the east. Birds, however, can negotiate these natural barriers—some do it as part of their breeding cycle—and representatives from both realms exist side by side. In this selection from Severtsov's work, the ibisbill and bar-headed goose (right) represent the east, and the tits (opposite) represent the west.

The ibisbill, a resident of the Himalayan foothills, goes to the high mountains to breed, siting its nests above 10,500 feet. The bar-headed goose has an even greater range, leaving the hot plains of northern India for the high lakes of Tibet and Turkestan. Its migration involves flying over the Himalayas, up to heights where survival seems impossible. This goose has been plotted on radar flying above the level at which man would die from lack of oxygen.

The page of drawings of tits is one of Severtsov's early attempts at classifying these birds. Long claws and bills enable some of them to perch on fragile leaves, picking off delicate insects, while those with heavier bills and shorter claws work through the secondary growth, feeding on larger insects. (Research done since Severtsov's day has shown that No. 2 is not a separate species but a juvenile of No. 8.).

IBISBILL (ABOVE) AND BAR-HEADED GOOSE

VARIETIES OF ASIAN PENDULINE TITS AND A LONG-TAILED TIT (NO.1) COMMON IN EUROPE

## The Fugitive Ox

The commonest animal in the Pamirs is the yak, for it is not only wild but also domesticated on a large scale. At the time when Severtsov did his drawing (right), wild yaks ranged from western Turkestan to China. Since then they have suffered by competition for limited grazing with their domesticated relatives, retreating to desolate mountain-top sanctuaries, where they live at heights of up to 20,000 feet.

Yaks are the most impressive members of the ox family. A big bull yak is jet-black, stands six feet eight inches at the shoulder, carries horns that span six feet and weighs three quarters of a ton. Yaks are protected by layers of long fine hair which form a thick coat and hang down along the stomach as a "kilt" to keep the legs warm. For food they make do with the tougher grazing nearest the snow-line, moving down a little in winter to eat the remnants of alpine summer pasture buried beneath the snow. They get at these meagre rations by scraping the snow away with their hooves or by moving into areas exposed by avalanches. They descend farthest at the end of winter, gathering just below the spring snow-line to crop the lush new growth.

Here wild and domesticated yaks mingle, the latter forming the vast majority of the huge herds and the former, through interbreeding, re-introducing strength and agility to often jaded stock in a service much valued by herdsmen.

*YAK BULL*

PERSIAN GAZELLE

## The Mountain Climbers

Like many large animals that live in the mountains, the Persian gazelle (left) and the Marco Polo sheep (opposite) are both highly mobile, for their environment is constantly changing. Succulent pastures may be coated with ice overnight and springtime streams of melt-water disappear in autumn as the peaks freeze solid once again.

These two animals are constantly on the move, searching for food and breeding grounds while avoiding the severest temperatures. The gazelle was tracked down by Przhevalsky among the spiky, shattered outcrops where desert meets mountain, and followed to an altitude of about 4,500 feet. The Marco Polo, the world's largest sheep, grazes the higher slopes at about 16,000 feet in the Pamir valleys. Severtsov found the Marco Polo (named after the famous explorer who discovered it) exploiting the sparse vegetation close to the snow-line. It walks unerringly along the sharp ridges and negotiates the broken screes at the heads of valleys with ease as it pursues its daily routine. The sheep feeds in the early morning, moves to a warm spot to chew and rest by day, and finally retires to a well-sheltered heap of boulders to spend the night in relative safety.

MARCO POLO SHEEP

# 7/ The Mirror in the Sky

*The sapphire waters of Issyk-Kul rival the sky blue of Lake Geneva . . . beyond there stretch the Tien Shan giants bathed in bright sunlight, silhouetted against the deep blue sky of Central Asia.* P. P. SEMYONOV TIEN-SHANSKY/ *TRAVELS IN THE TIEN SHAN*

High up in the middle of the Tien Shan, between the Kungey-Alatau and Terskey-Alatau ranges of Kirgizia, lies Lake Issyk-Kul, which local people call "The Mirror in the Sky". Local legend says that the Great Ruler of the Mountain Spirits placed the lake in the mountains so that his bride could look into it and admire her own beauty. It is a remarkable body of water. With a length of 111 miles and a width of 37 miles, it is the second largest mountain lake in the world, after Titicaca in the Andes. It has a unique, warm climate—Issyk-Kul means "warm lake"—and as a result has its own miniature ecology. From the time I first heard of Issyk-Kul, I knew I could never leave Turkestan without seeing it.

There were personal reasons, too, for my interest. I have always been fascinated by lakes, ever since my childhood near Lake Baikal in Siberia. To me lakes are the most admirable physical features of our planet, and the most interesting kind of water. Seas are huge and impersonal; rivers are mercurial—it takes hundreds of miles to get the feel of a river; but lakes are stable, accessible and intimate. They can be examined at leisure from all angles and distances. And mountain lakes in particular, bringing warmth to an otherwise cold landscape, hold a strong charm for me. In addition, I had read a 19th-Century account of a rare toxic plant—"the Issyk-Kul root"—and, with all the optimism of total ignorance, I was keen to find it and identify it. At dawn one day during my last week in Turkestan, I left the town of Frunze and took the bus to Rybachye, the administrative centre of the Issyk-Kul region.

The lake is so extraordinary that it has prompted numerous other legends—besides the "Mirror in the Sky" story—to account for its origins. My favourite is a local version of the Midas story. According to this legend, the Ussuns, a people preceding the Kirgiz, once had as their ruler a king, immensely rich, who devoted himself almost totally to the happiness of his people. He lived in a splendid palace, where he lavished hospitality on all and sundry. He had only one fault: he demanded a new barber every morning, and then had each barber killed by the evening. The profession became understandably unpopular; and in the end there was only one barber left in the whole country. He was summoned to the palace, and since he was now the only barber, he survived. Soon, however, he became tormented by a dreadful secret he would not mention. At last, he went to see a hermit in the mountains, and confessed to him what tormented him so. To rid him of the secret that weighed him down, the hermit counselled him to whisper it down a well, then carefully replace the cover of the well. This the barber did. He went to the well, and three times in succession cried into it: "Our good king has ass's-ears", after which he fled so hastily that he forgot to shut the lid. Then the water in the well rose, drowned the splendid palace and inundated the whole land—to become Lake Issyk-Kul.

The real origins of the great lake are no less interesting. A series of earth movements 25 million years ago created the great oval depression, some 155 miles long and 55 miles wide, part of which today contains the lake. The depression filled with the melt-water from the surrounding mountains and then, with the coming of the Ice Age, froze solid. For tens of thousands of years each year's snowfall piled on top of the previous year's unmelted snow, and formed hundreds of feet of solid ice. Finally, when the ice and snow began their final retreat some 10,000 years ago, the water flowed away over Issyk-Kul's basin rim and then dropped steadily to its present level.

Although a river must once have drained the lake, no river flows out now and the water from the 44 rivers that enter it is balanced only by the intense summer evaporation. By a wonderful piece of natural economy, however, none of the water vapour rising from the lake is wasted. It is caught by the two high mountain ranges flanking the lake, and there it soon turns to rain or snow. During the spring, and sometimes in summer, after a bright and sunny morning, clouds begin to appear near the mountain tops in the early afternoon. They are first a light colour, but soon turn to deep violet. Snow falls, changing to rain at lower altitudes, and the lake's water is thus recycled. Local patriots claim, that over the lake—the stored heat of which may well ensure a rising column of air— no rain ever falls and there is always a blue window over the centre.

I took the bus from Frunze to Rybachye along a canyon that led up towards Issyk-Kul. It was springtime, and the turbulent mountain water had toppled rocks from the canyon walls as it rolled down towards the highway. Along the water's edge sprouted the first pale blue blades of grass, and under the trees, lightly clad in still transparent leaves, tulips were just beginning to open.

My companion and guide, who was wildly enthusiastic about the beauty of his native landscape, insisted on our leaving the bus a few hundred yards before the road emerged from the canyon, and walking the last few miles to Rybachye along the lake-side. "Only then will you be able to appreciate the incredible beauty which will unfold before your eyes," he promised.

After this kind of dramatic build-up, my first reaction was that of disappointment. The scene appeared to be distinctly desert-like: a very low pebbly shore with long sandy spits extending far into the water. Very scanty vegetation—grass between the stones and reeds along the water edge. The lake itself appeared to be a rather narrow inlet hemmed in by low bare hills from two sides. Only straight ahead did the water stretch on towards the horizon, where it merged with violet mist—I could not, of course, see the eastern end of the lake, some 110 miles away from where we stood. None of the snow-capped mountains that flank the lake were visible from here. The water was calm, and it looked heavy; there were thin ripples some distance off shore, but near the shore itself the water, still only lightly touched by the misty sun behind me, appeared to be immobile. It all seemed rather desolate.

"What do you think of it?" My companion asked eagerly.

"It's pretty," I said uncertainly.

"This is the flattest and driest end," my friend said defensively. "Walk with me a kilometer or two and you'll see the lake better. But it is the other end that is really beautiful. Do you know that we have twice as much rain there as at this end? It's a fact. Here it is practically a desert."

So we started on what proved to be a tiring walk along the pebbly shore, and as we walked the landscape started to change. Some clumps of grass appeared between the stones, and at one point we saw several yellow tulips ready to open up.

"And where do you grow those opium poppies?" I asked breezily.

I knew that the Issyk-Kul was the only place in the Soviet Union where such poppies were cultivated. The question upset my companion.

"They are not *opium* poppies," he said. "They are medicinal ones. They are used exclusively for our pharmaceutical industries. Opium, in some form, is used in over 90 per cent of all medical preparations."

"I know," I said, "but where are they?"

"On the other side." My friend made a wide gesture towards the horizon. "But please don't think that we smoke opium like the Chinese or the Afghans. Lenin said that the proletariat doesn't need artificial stimulation." In other words, opium is not the religion of the people.

As we walked along the shore towards Rybachye and the white contours of the two ranges flanking the lake began to appear through the haze, my companion told me about the peculiarities of the Issyk-Kul "cauldron"—a little world of its own. Almost all animals, besides typically desert ones, could be found here, and also over 3,500 plants and trees—making Issyk-Kul a museum of Tien Shan flora.

"Do you still have the Issyk-Kul root here?" I asked my companion.

The question drew a blank. Indeed, all I knew of this toxic plant was contained in an account by P. S. Nazarov, a 19th-Century authority on Turkestan flora. "It is enough to sit for but a short time near its handsome dark blue flowers to get a bad headache," Nazarov wrote. "The root, dried and pounded into a powder, is a fearful poison. Not a few natives of Turkestan have been dispatched to the other world by means of this plant. The local women have an original method of packing off unwanted husbands without giving rise to any suspicion. To do this they make an infusion of the root, and in it soak a shirt belonging to the victim whom they propose to dispatch from this sinful world, dry it, iron it out and give it to him to put on after his bath when the pores of the skin are open. The venom is absorbed into the blood, the victim sickens and in a couple of months, or three at the outside, gives up the ghost in the most natural manner in the world."

Unfortunately Nazarov gave no botanical name of the plant, but I had a very strong suspicion that it was either *Aconitum napellus* or *Aconitum sibiricum*, a native of Siberia, and a remarkable plant indeed. Growing to a height of seven feet, it has often proved fatal to young cattle eating it (mature animals never touch it), and so it has been almost exterminated by Siberian cattle-breeders.

Why would I, a happily married man, be interested in this terrible plant? The answer was simple: the aconite root, properly used for medicinal purposes, is claimed as a true miracle drug for arthritis.

At the western neck of Lake Issyk-Kul, brackish water breaks fitfully over debris washed down from the Tien Shan mountain range, visible in the background. The lake has receded to its present 111-mile length in an oval depression created by earth movements 25 million years ago. Now its level is stable, intense summer evaporation balancing the inflow of water from a total of 44 rivers and streams.

I tried to describe the plant to my friend, and after a few guesses, he suddenly brightened up: "Wait a minute! I remember my father telling me about the *Shaitan* root—the "devil" root—which old Kirgiz witches sold to unhappy lovers wishing to get rid of their rivals! It was also known as the 'Imam's turban'."

That rang a bell. Aconite was often called "monk's hood"—and *Imam* was a muslim word for a priest. Could this be the same thing?

My friend felt sure that the plant could no longer be found in the Issyk-Kul region, since it was now a prime cattle-raising area of Kirgizia. The cattlemen would long since have exterminated it. In fact, he thought this was just a part of the local folklore, a mere legend. But I knew that if I could find a true *Aconitum sibiricum* I could cure a few of my arthritic friends and, with luck, retire in comfort.

As the day wore on and we neared Rybachye, it became quite warm, and I attempted to remove my shirt. My guide restrained me, almost by force. "The Issyk-Kul sun will kill you!" he remonstrated. Any exposure to the sun up there causes severe burns, he said, even on a cloudy day. All people coming here for the first time are warned against any prolonged exposure. We were told that hospitals around the lake are filled each summer with fool-hardy tourists coming here from northern Russia, all being treated for sun-burn. In July or August any exposure for a longer period than ten minutes is dangerous, and even in spring or autumn prolonged exposure is not recommended.

From Rybachye, I spent a couple of days exploring the lake's shore and mountain slopes. I tramped through the glades, meadows, and along wooded canyons. I breathed in the mountain air and listened to the haunting mountain sounds: an occasional rock rolling down-hill, a tree branch breaking, the cry of an unseen creature scurrying through the shrubs, a sudden gust of wind brushing the tree tops. Among the tall grasses, I could hear slight movements as pheasants, crane, heron and woodcock withdrew at my approach. Never had I had such a strong feeling of peace as in this rare setting, which was everywhere permeated with the salty freshness of the great lake.

Once, I thought that I had at last found a real Siberian aconite plant, the "Issyk-Kul root", growing between some rocks. It stood about five feet high and had some bluish buds. The local guide who was with me shocked me—I suspect intentionally—by picking up some of the buds and chewing them. I was fully prepared to see him drop dead, but he simply laughed when I shouted to him to stop committing suicide. On closer examination it was nothing but a local wild iris. "Good for your stomach," the guide said rubbing his midriff. "Makes worms go away!" With a wry smile at my own previous optimism, I abandoned hope of seeing the "Issyk-Kul root".

I had no intention of attempting to scale any of the heights that lay nearby, though had I been younger I would have been tempted. Mountain climbers can reach these peaks without too much difficulty and those who have been up there claim that an almost psychedelic world unravels before them. The entire Issyk-Kul wonderland lies at their feet and the great lake glistens in the sun, like a real mirror in the sky. To the south stretches the most dramatic part of the Tien Shan, with endless mountain ridges reaching off over the horizon. The grandiose Kokshaal-Tau, the spinal column of the entire system, rises as a sparkling backdrop to this enchanted scene. And on a clear day, they can see right across to the Khan Tengri, set in its cluster of frozen peaks, the most impressive mountain knot of the Tien Shan.

I'll have to take their word for it. I like to think, however, that my own final view of Issyk-Kul and its mountains rivalled the experiences of any mountaineer. On my last day, as my flight back to Moscow took off from Frunze, I watched the mountains recede and flatten beneath me. Perhaps because I knew this was my last look at Turkestan, this seemed to be the most soul-stirring view of my entire trip: isolated among the brilliant icy ridges, the giant mirror glistened in the sun and seemed indeed, to have been placed there to reflect the spirit of the mountains.

# The Snowy Slopes of the Tien Shan

The arid expanses of the Turkestan wilderness depend for their water on the great mountain masses to their east. One of the most dramatic of these sources is the Tien Shan, a range north-east of the Pamirs, whose alpine glaciers and high perennial snowfields melt into streams to feed the parched deserts and steppes below. The juxtaposition of snowfields and the grassy slopes that result from this abundance of water creates a rare landscape, captured by the Russian photographer, Lev Ustinov, in this series of pictures taken from a helicopter.

Since the Tien Shan are young mountains, erosion is still in its early stages. Summer streams incise and exaggerate the valleys, freezing in winter to an iced tracery stretching down the mountainsides. Snow seeps into the bedrock as it melts in the sun and then breaks rock-chips loose when it freezes and expands at night. In winter, icefields of compacted snow slip downwards, making the nights eerie as they groan and scrape into the valleys.

For Ustinov and the helicopter crew, buffeted by sharp air currents, the flight through this jagged landscape was a "circus performance", as hair-raising as a tight-rope act.

Lack of high-altitude oxygen equipment forced them to swoop through valleys so narrow they felt they could reach over and touch the mountain walls. The noise of their motors caused small avalanches to cascade down sheer cliffs. Often the landscape was shrouded in a spring haze, but where the air cleared they had some breathtaking views: a cliff frosted with a thin line of ice, alpine meadows splattered with snow, valley sides scored by frozen streams and, lower down, trickling brooks that glinted in the sun. To Ustinov the ice looked like a network of veins and arteries on some vast anatomical chart of the human body.

His photographs capture the sharp, clear colours and varying textures of the mountain scene. The grass, even and lush on plunging slopes, conjures up visions of golf-course fairways laid out by some fanatical groundsman. The clean edges of snow become bas-reliefs of purest marble. Blue-green feathery tufts of coniferous trees such as spruce, fir and juniper soften the bare hillsides in places, but elsewhere rocks jut roughly through the grass and sharp ridges pierce the ice as a reminder of the mountains' essential severity.

SNOW-FROSTED MOUNTAIN RIDGES

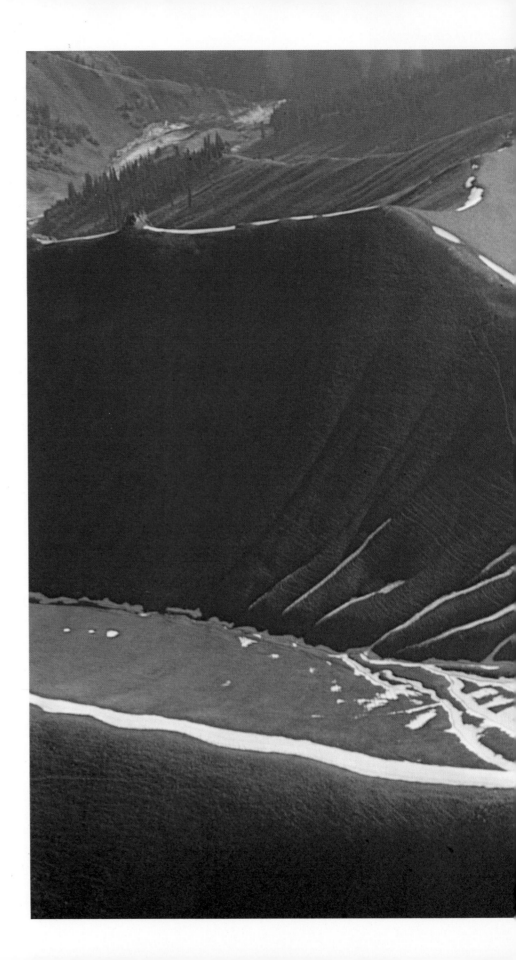

*FROZEN DRAINAGE PATTERN*

SOLID STREAMS OF ICE

*THE MOUNTAINS' SNOWCAP*

MEETING OF GREEN AND WHITE

# Bibliography

Allworth, Edward, (Ed.), *Central Asia, a Century of Russian Rule.* Columbia University Press, 1967.

Bacon, Elizabeth E., *Central Asians under Russian Rule.* Cornell University Press, 1966.

Burnaby, Capt. F. G., *A Ride to Khiva; Travels and Adventures in Central Asia.* Cassell, 1876.

Carruthers, Douglas, *Beyond the Caspian.* Oliver and Boyd, 1949.

Curtis, William Eleroy, *Turkestan, the Heart of Asia.* Hodder and Stoughton, 1911.

Curzon, George N., *Russia in Central Asia.* Longmans, Green and Co., 1889.

Curzon, George N., *The Pamirs and the Source of the Oxus.* The Royal Geographical Society, 1896.

Dunmore, the Earl of, *The Pamirs* (2 vols.). John Murray, 1893.

Etherton, P. T., *Across the Roof of the World.* Constable, 1911.

Gordon, Lieut. Col. T. E., *The Roof of the World.* Edmonston and Douglas, 1876.

Hedin, Sven, *Through Asia* (2 vols.). Methuen, 1898.

Krader, Lawrence, *Peoples of Central Asia.* Indiana University Publications, 1962.

MacGahan, J. A., *Campaigning on the Oxus.* Central Asian Library, 1874.

Marvin, Charles, *The Russian Campaign Against the Turkomens.* W. H. Allen, 1880.

Massey Stewart, John, *Across the Russias.* Harvill Press, 1969.

Olufsen, O., *Through the Unknown Pamirs.* William Heinemann, 1904.

Petrov, M. P., *Deserts of Central Asia,* (2 vols. in Russian). Academy of Sciences of the U.S.S.R., 1966-67.

Polo, Marco, *Travels.* Penguin Books, 1965 (paperback).

Przhevalsky, N., *Mongolia* (2 vols., in Russian). St Petersburg, 1875.

St. George, George, *Russia.* B. T. Batsford Ltd., 1973.

Suslov, S. P., *Physical Geography of Asiatic Russia.* W. H. Freeman and Co., 1961.

Vaidyanath, R., *Formation of Soviet Central Asian Republics.* People's Publishing House, New Delhi, 1967.

van der Post, Laurens, *Journey into Russia.* The Hogarth Press, 1964.

Wheeler, Geoffrey, *The Modern History of Soviet Central Asia.* Weidenfeld and Nicolson, 1964.

Wood, Captain J., *A Personal Narrative of a Journey to the Source of the River Oxus.* John Murray, 1841.

# Acknowledgements

The author and editors of this book wish to thank the following: Prof. M. Abdallin, Tashkent; V. K. Boichenko, Intourist, Moscow; Martin Brendell, British Museum (Natural History), London; Dr. C. Embleton, London; Tatiana Georgievna, Tashkent; Prof. Goncharov, Tashkent; Christopher Grey-Wilson, Royal Botanical Gardens, Kew; Nicholas Guppy, London; Prof. M. Habyiev, Tashkent; David Hollis, British Museum (Natural History), London; Dr. C. Humphries, London; Dr. I. Ilyinsky, Tashkent; Prof. I. Iomudsky, Ashkhabad; Mr. P. Ionov, Novosti Press Agency, Ashkhabad; Dr. H. Kamaev, Tashkent; Prof. S. V. Komarov, All-Union Institute of Cinematography, Moscow; Dr. Lydia Kulbashnaya, Tashkent; Dr. M. Kurmaev, Tashkent; John Massey Stewart, London; L. G. Mikhailov, Intourist, Moscow; S. V. Mikhalkov, Moscow; Dr. M. Mirzaev, Tashkent; Caroline Pope, Royal Botanical Gardens, Kew; A. E. Porazhniakov, Novosti Press Agency, Moscow; S. Rashidov, Novosti Press Agency, Tashkent; Academician F. N. Rusanov, Tashkent; Prof. A. Rustamov, Ashkhabad; Arkady Semonian, Moscow; I. I. Udaltzov, Novosti Press Agency, Moscow; Dr. K. Zakirov, Tashkent.

# Picture Credits

*The photographs in this book are from the Novosti Press Agency, Moscow, with the exception of the following:*

24–*Ritratti di Cento Capitani*, Capriolo, 1600. 80/81–by Dan Freeman, from Bruce Coleman Ltd., London. 149–*Nouvelle Géographie Universelle*, Vol VI, Elisée Reclus, 1881. 152–*Puteshestvic U Tyan-Shan*, Semyonov Tien-Shansky, 1948. 154–*Das 19te Jahrhundert in Bildnissen*, Werckmeister, 1901. 157 to 159–*Vertical and Horizontal Distribution of Turkestan Animals*, N. A. Severtsov, 1873. 160 to 163–*Mongolia y strana tangoustov*, N. Przhevalsky, 1875/6.

# Index

*Numerals in italics indicate a
photograph or drawing of the subject
mentioned.*

**XXXXXXX**
Colour reproduction by P.D.I. Ltd., Leeds, England—a Time Inc. subsidiary.
Filmsetting by C. E. Dawkins (Typesetters) Ltd., London, SE1 1UN.
Printed and bound in Belgium by Brepols S.A.—Turnhout.